Special Functions of
Mathematical Physics

Athena Series

SELECTED TOPICS IN MATHEMATICS

Edwin Hewitt, *Editor*

Harry Hochstadt

Polytechnic Institute of Brooklyn

Special Functions of Mathematical Physics

HOLT, RINEHART AND WINSTON

New York • Chicago • San Francisco

Toronto • London

October, 1966

Copyright © 1961 by

Holt, Rinehart and Winston, Inc.

Library of Congress Catalog Card Number: 61-7857

23673-0111

Printed in the United States of America

Preface

The purpose of this book is to introduce students of mathematics, physics, and engineering to some of the special functions of mathematical physics. The chief aim is to provide a background for the proper understanding of these functions. In such a short volume one can hardly hope to develop as many of the important properties of these functions as one would like. Fortunately, there exist numerous compilations of such properties. The two most worthy of mention are *Formulas and Theorems for the Special Functions of Mathematical Physics* by W. Magnus and F. Oberhettinger, and the three volumes of *Higher Transcendental Functions* by A. Erdélyi, W. Magnus, F. Oberhettinger, and F. G. Tricomi. The reader who has little or no prior acquaintance with these topics is therefore urged to examine these volumes after reading this book to acquire some feeling for the wealth of material available. It is hoped that this book will help the reader to go on to more advanced treatises with ease.

The author would like to express his gratitude to Professor W. Magnus, who first as lecturer and later as a colleague helped to arouse and stimulate his liking for these topics. Professor Magnus was also kind enough to read the manuscript, and his suggestions and comments were gratefully accepted.

H. H.

Brooklyn, New York
April, 1961

Contents

Chapter 4. Mathieu Functions

Special Functions of
Mathematical Physics

[1]

Orthogonal Polynomials

1. Definition

Many of the functions that occur in mathematical physics belong to families of so-called orthogonal systems. We will furnish the following definition for such systems:

A system of real functions $\phi_0(x)$, $\phi_1(x)$, $\phi_2(x)$, $\phi_3(x)$, $\cdots$ *will be said to be orthogonal over an interval* $a \leq x \leq b$, *with weight function* $w(x)$, *if*

$$\int_a^b w(x)\, \phi_i(x)\, \phi_j(x)\, dx = 0, \qquad i \neq j.$$

Here $w(x)$ is nonnegative in the interval of integration, and, furthermore, all specified integrals must exist.

Such a system may have a finite or infinite number of members, and the interval (a, b) may be finite or infinite. If we stipulate in addition that

$$\int_a^b w(x)\, \phi_i^2(x)\, dx = 1, \qquad i = 0, 1, 2, \cdots,$$

we will call the system orthonormal.

In this chapter we will concern ourselves with systems where all $\phi_i(x)$ are polynomials.

2. Construction of Systems of Orthogonal Functions

Once a weight function $w(x)$ and an interval are specified, we can construct a system of orthogonal polynomials. We select $\phi_0(x) = 1$, and now seek a linear function $\phi_1(x)$ so that

$$\int_a^b w(x)\, \phi_0(x)\, \phi_1(x)\, dx = 0.$$

This is one equation in two unknowns, and we can certainly find a $\phi_1(x)$ now. If we wish the solution to be unique we must impose some other condition on $\phi_1(x)$, such as, for example, the normalizing condition

$$\int_a^b w(x)\, \phi_1^2(x)\, dx = 1.$$

1

Without such a condition there will be many solutions, but they all will be multiples of one basic solution. To find $\phi_2(x)$ we now impose the conditions

$$\int_a^b w(x)\, \phi_0(x)\, \phi_2(x)\, dx = 0$$

$$\int_a^b w(x)\, \phi_1(x)\, \phi_2(x)\, dx = 0,$$

where $\phi_2(x)$ is a second-degree polynomial. Here, as before, these equations determine $\phi_2(x)$ within a constant multiple. In general, to find $\phi_N(x)$ we choose a polynomial of degree N, subject to

$$\int_a^b w(x)\, \phi_i(x)\, \phi_N(x)\, dx = 0, \qquad i = 0, 1, 2, \cdots, N-1.$$

These N equations determine $\phi_N(x)$ within a constant multiplier. It is evident that one can now represent any power of x in terms of a finite series of $\phi_i(x)$, so that

$$x^k = a_0\phi_0(x) + a_1\phi_1(x) + \cdots + a_k\phi_k(x).$$

Use of the orthogonality property of these functions allows one to determine the coefficients so that

$$a_j = \frac{\int_a^b w(x)\, x^k\, \phi_j(x)\, dx}{\int_a^b w(x)\, \phi_j^2(x)\, dx}.$$

It follows therefore that

$$\int_a^b w(x)\, x^i\, \phi_N(x)\, dx = 0, \qquad i = 0, 1, 2, \cdots, N-1.$$

Conversely, these N equations can be used to determine $\phi_N(x)$ within an arbitrary multiplier. It should be shown that these N equations are really independent; the proof of this can be found in note 1 of the appendix to Chapter 1. It also follows that $\phi_N(x)$ is orthogonal to every polynomial of degree less than N.

3. Examples of Orthogonal Polynomials

Particular examples* of such orthogonal polynomials are the following cases.

I. Let

$$a = -1, b = 1, w(x) = (1-x)^\alpha(1+x)^\beta, \alpha > -1, \beta > -1.$$

Then $\phi_n(x)$ is called the Jacobi polynomial and is designated by $P_n^{(\alpha,\beta)}(x)$. When $\alpha = \beta$ they are called ultraspherical polynomials, and particular cases are:

---

* For purposes of reference and consistency the notation used follows as far as possible *Formulas and Theorems for the Special Functions of Mathematical Physics* by W. Magnus and F. Oberhettinger, New York, 1949.

a) Let

$$\alpha = \beta = -\tfrac{1}{2}.$$

Then

$$P_n^{(-\frac{1}{2},-\frac{1}{2})}(x) = \frac{(2n)!}{2^{2n}(n!)^2} T_n(x),$$

the Tchebichef polynomials of the first kind.

b) Let

$$a = \beta = 0$$

Then

$$P_n^{(0,0)}(x) = P_n(x),$$

the Legendre polynomials.

II. Let

$$a = 0, b = +\infty, w(x) = x^\alpha e^{-x}, \qquad \alpha > -1.$$

Then

$$\phi_n(x) = L_n^{(\alpha)}(x),$$

the Laguerre polynomials.

III. Let

$$a = -\infty, b = +\infty, w(x) = e^{-x^2/2}.$$

Then

$$\phi_n(x) = H_n(x),$$

the Hermite polynomials.

4. Existence of Recursion Formulas

We will now show that all orthogonal polynomials satisfy a recursion formula of the type

$$\phi_{N+1}(x) - (A_N x + B_N)\,\phi_N(x) + C_N\phi_{N-1}(x) = 0.$$

To prove this statement we first choose A_N so that

$$\phi_{N+1}(x) - x\,A_N\,\phi_N(x)$$

is of at most the degree N; that is, the x^{N+1} terms cancel. Therefore one can write

$$\phi_{N+1}(x) - x\,A_N\,\phi_N(x) = \sum_{j=0}^{N} \alpha_j\,\phi_j(x).$$

To evaluate a particular coefficient α_i, we multiply both sides by $w(x) \, \phi_i(x)$ and integrate over the interval (a, b). Use of the orthogonality of these functions leads to

$$\alpha_i = \frac{\int_a^b w(x) \left[\phi_{N+1}(x) - x A_N \phi_N(x)\right] \phi_i(x) \, dx}{\int_a^b w(x) \, \phi_i^2(x) \, dx}$$

$$= - A_N \frac{\int_a^b x \, w(x) \, \phi_N(x) \, \phi_i(x) \, dx}{\int_a^b w(x) \, \phi_i^2(x) \, dx}.$$

The term $x\phi_i(x)$ is a polynomial of degree $i + 1$, and since $\phi_N(x)$ is orthogonal to every polynomial of degree less than N, it follows that

$$\int_a^b w(x) \left[x \, \phi_i(x)\right] \phi_N(x) \, dx = 0, \qquad i = 0, 1, 2, \cdots, N - 2.$$

Therefore the only nonvanishing coefficients are α_{N-1} and α_N. Thus

$$\phi_{N+1}(x) - x A_N \phi_N(x) = \alpha_{N-1} \phi_{N-1}(x) + \alpha_N \phi_N(x),$$

which, in effect, proves the statement.

5. Differential Equations Satisfied by the Orthogonal Polynomials

We will now show that certain of these functions also satisfy second-order linear differential equations. In particular we will deal, first, with the Jacobi polynomials. We consider the expression

$$\frac{d}{dx} \left[(1 - x^2)(1 - x)^\alpha(1 + x)^\beta \frac{d}{dx} P_n^{(\alpha,\beta)}(x)\right]$$

and its expanded form

$$(1 - x)^\alpha(1 + x)^\beta \left[(1 - x^2)\frac{d^2}{dx^2} P_n^{(\alpha,\beta)}(x) - (2x + \beta x + \alpha x + \beta - \alpha)\frac{d}{dx} P_n^{(\alpha,\beta)}(x)\right]$$

and observe that the bracketed expression of the latter form is simply a polynomial of degree n. Therefore we can write

$$\frac{d}{dx} \left[(1 - x^2) (1 - x)^\alpha(1 + x)^\beta \frac{d}{dx} P_n^{(\alpha,\beta)}(x)\right] = (1 - x)^\alpha(1 + x)^\beta \sum_{i=0}^{n} \alpha_i P_i^{(\alpha,\beta)}(x).$$

We can now solve for the coefficients α_i in the standard manner and find

$$\alpha_i = \frac{\int_{-1}^1 P_i^{(\alpha,\beta)}(x) \frac{d}{dx} \left[(1 - x^2) (1 - x)^\alpha(1 + x)^\beta \frac{d}{dx} P_n^{(\alpha,\beta)}(x)\right] dx}{\int_{-1}^1 (1 - x)^\alpha(1 + x)^\beta \left[P_i^{(\alpha,\beta)}(x)\right]^2 dx}.$$

The numerator becomes, after integrating by parts twice,

$$\int_{-1}^{1} P_n^{(\alpha,\beta)}(x) \frac{d}{dx} \left[(1 - x^2) (1 - x)^\alpha (1 + x)^\beta \frac{d}{dx} P_i^{(\alpha,\beta)}(x) \right] dx,$$

which can be rewritten in the form

$$\int_{-1}^{1} (1 - x)^\alpha (1 + x)^\beta P_n^{(\alpha,\beta)}(x) \left[(1 - x^2) \frac{d^2}{dx^2} P_i^{(\alpha,\beta)}(x) \right.$$
$$\left. - (2x + \beta x + \alpha x + \beta - \alpha) \frac{d}{dx} P_i^{(\alpha,\beta)}(x) \right] dx.$$

The expression in the bracket is a polynomial of degree i, which must be orthogonal to $P_n^{(\alpha,\beta)}(x)$ if $i < n$. Therefore $\alpha_i = 0$, $i = 0, 1, 2, \cdots, n - 1$, and we have

$$(1 - x)^\alpha (1 + x)^\beta \left[(1 - x^2) \frac{d^2}{dx^2} P_n^{(\alpha,\beta)}(x) - (2x + \beta x + \alpha x + \beta - \alpha) \frac{d}{dx} P_n^{(\alpha,\beta)}(x) \right]$$
$$= (1 - x)^\alpha (1 + x)^\beta \alpha_n P_n^{(\alpha,\beta)}(x).$$

To evaluate α_n conveniently we use the fact that $P_n^{(\alpha,\beta)}(x)$ is a polynomial of degree n, and by comparing the coefficients of x^n, after cancellation of $(1 - x)^\alpha (1 + x)^\beta$ we find that $P_n^{(\alpha,\beta)}(x)$ satisfies the differential equation

$$(1 - x^2)y'' + [(\beta - \alpha) - (\alpha + \beta + 2)x]y' + n(n + \alpha + \beta + 1)y = 0.$$

In particular the Tchebichef polynomials satisfy

$$(1 - x^2)y'' - xy' + n^2 y = 0$$

and the Legendre polynomials

$$(1 - x^2)y'' - 2xy' + n(n + 1)y = 0.$$

By an analogous argument we can start with the expression

$$\frac{d}{dx} \left[x\, x^\alpha\, e^{-x} \frac{d}{dx} L_n^{(\alpha)}(x) \right]$$

and show that the Laguerre polynomials satisfy the differential equation

$$xy'' + (\alpha + 1 - x)y' + ny = 0.$$

Similarly, by starting with

$$\frac{d}{dx} \left[e^{-x^2/2} \frac{d}{dx} H_n(x) \right]$$

we find that the Hermite polynomials satisfy the equation

$$y'' - xy' + ny = 0.$$

6. Recursion Formulas of the Classical Orthogonal Polynomials

We have seen that the orthogonality requirement did not determine the $\phi_N(x)$ uniquely, but only within a constant multiple. Nevertheless, the differential equations corresponding to these $\phi_N(x)$ are fully determined, since if any $\phi_N(x)$ satisfies them, so will $c\phi_N(x)$.

The situation regarding the recursion formulas is different. There we find that the coefficients depend very strongly on the choice of the multiplier. To derive the recursion formula for the Legendre polynomials we follow the convention that

$$P_n(x) = \frac{(2n)!}{2^n n!^2} \left[x^n + \cdots \right].$$

To evaluate the coefficients of the lower powers of x we can insert a general polynomial into the differential equation (Sec. 5) and use the method of undetermined coefficients to evaluate them. Thus we find that

$$P_n(x) = \frac{(2n)!}{2^n n!^2} \left[x^n - \frac{n(n-1)}{2(2n-1)} x^{n-2} + \frac{n(n-1)(n-2)(n-3)}{2 \cdot 4 \cdot (2n-1)(2n-3)} x^{n-4} - \cdots \right].$$

To evaluate the coefficients A_N, B_N, C_N in the recursion formula (Sec. 4) we replace $P_{n+1}(x)$, $P_n(x)$, $P_{n-1}(x)$ by their series and again use the method of undetermined coefficients. We then find that

$$(n + 1) P_{n+1}(x) - (2n + 1) x P_n(x) + n P_{n-1}(x) = 0.$$

Similarly, we follow the convention that

$$T_n(x) = 2^{n-1} x^n + \cdots, \qquad n \geq 1$$
$$= 1, \qquad n = 0$$

and find

$$T_{n+1}(x) - 2x T_n(x) + T_{n-1}(x) = 0.$$

For the Laguerre polynomials we have

$$L_n^{(\alpha)}(x) = \frac{(-1)^n x^n}{n!} + \cdots$$

so that

$$(n + 1) L_{n+1}^{(\alpha)}(x) + (x - 2n - 1 - \alpha) L_n^{(\alpha)}(x) + (n + \alpha) L_{n-1}^{(\alpha)}(x) = 0,$$

and for the Hermite polynomials

$$H_n(x) = x^n + \cdots$$

so that

$$H_{n+1}(x) - x\,H_n(x) + n\,H_{n-1}(x) = 0.$$

It is evident that once $\phi_0(x)$ and $\phi_1(x)$ are known, the recursion formulas provide a convenient method of finding other $\phi_N(x)$ recursively.

7. Zeros of Orthogonal Polynomials

Every polynomial of degree n must have, in accordance with the fundamental theorem of algebra, exactly n roots. In general, these roots may be complex, but we will prove that for orthogonal polynomials all roots must be real and distinct, and what is more, they must lie in the interval (a, b).
$\phi_N(x)$ must have at least one root in the interval since

$$\int_a^b w(x)\,\phi_0(x)\,\phi_N(x)\,dx = 0;$$

but $\phi_0(x)$ is a constant, and if $\phi_N(x)$ did not change sign at least once in the interval the integrand would be of one sign, which contradicts the fact that the integral is zero. If we designate the real roots of odd multiplicity—that is, simple roots, triple roots, quintuple roots, and so on—that lie in the interval (a, b), as $x_1, x_2, \cdots, x_l$, we see that the function

$$\phi_N(x)\,(x - x_1)\,(x - x_2)\cdots(x - x_l)$$

is either nonnegative or nonpositive, since this function now has roots of even multiplicity only, and at such a root the function has a maximum or minimum, but does not change sign. If $l < N$ it follows that

$$\int_a^b w(x)\,\phi_N(x)\,(x - x_1)\cdots(x - x_l)\,dx = 0$$

since $\phi_N(x)$ is orthogonal to every polynomial of lower degree than N. But the integrand is of constant sign, which contradicts the fact that the integral vanishes. Thus $l = N$, and therefore $\phi_N(x)$ has N real roots in the interval (a, b), which exhausts all roots of $\phi_N(x)$.

Since these N roots are of odd multiplicity, and there are at most N roots, it also follows that these are simple roots.

8. A Physical Interpretation of the Zeros of the Orthogonal Polynomials

The zeros of the Jacobi polynomials have a rather curious application in potential theory. Suppose we consider the interval $(-1, 1)$ and place two positive charges of strengths p and q at $+1$ and -1, respectively, and n-unit positive charges within the interval at $x_1, x_2, \cdots, x_n$. The point of equilibrium corresponds to the condition for which the potential energy has a minimum. The potential energy of such a system is given by

$$\log T^{-1},$$

where

$$T = \prod_{k=1}^{n} (1 - x_k)^p (1 + x_k)^q \prod_{\substack{v,u=1,2\cdots,n \\ v<u}} |x_v - x_u|$$

and a necessary condition for minimum potential energy becomes

$$\frac{\partial}{\partial x_j} \log T^{-1} = 0, \qquad j = 1, 2, \cdots, n.$$

The evaluation of these derivatives leads to the system of equations

$$\frac{1}{x_i - x_1} + \frac{1}{x_j - x_2} + \cdots + \frac{1}{x_j - x_{j-1}} + \frac{1}{x_j - x_{j+1}}$$

$$+ \cdots + \frac{1}{x_j - x_n} + \frac{p}{x_j - 1} + \frac{q}{x_j + 1} = 0, \qquad j = 1, 2, \cdots, n.$$

We now introduce the polynomial

$$f(x) = (x - x_1) \cdots (x - x_n)$$

and observe that the above system of equations may be rewritten in the form

$$\frac{1}{2} \frac{f''(x_j)}{f'(x_j)} + \frac{p}{x_j - 1} + \frac{q}{x_j + 1} = 0,$$

which equation may be rearranged as

$$(1 - x_j^2)f''(x_j) + \left\{2q - 2p - (2q + 2p) x_j\right\} f'(x_j) = 0.$$

We now observe that the expression

$$(1 - x^2)f''(x) + \left\{2q - 2p - (2q + 2p) x\right\} f'(x)$$

must be a polynomial of degree n, whose roots are $x_1, x_2, \cdots, x_n$; in other words, the expression is a multiple of $f(x)$. If we let

$$(1 - x^2)f''(x) + \left\{2q - 2p - (2q + 2p) x\right\} f'(x) = cf(x)$$

we can find c by letting

$$f(x) = x^n + \cdots$$

and comparing coefficients of x^n. Then we find that

$$(1 - x^2)f''(x) + \{2q - 2p - (2q + 2p) x\}f'(x)$$
$$+ n\{2q + 2p + n - 1\}f(x) = 0.$$

This is precisely an equation (Sec. 5) whose solution is a Jacobi polynomial $P_n^{(2p-1,2q-1)}(x)$. Thus we see that the zeros of this Jacobi polynomial correspond to the equilibrium of the physical system under consideration.

9. Rodrigues' Formulas

We will now derive certain explicit representations of these orthogonal polynomials. We will show that

$$P_n^{(\alpha,\beta)} = \frac{(-1)^n}{2^n n!(1 - x)^\alpha(1 + x)^\beta} \frac{d^n}{dx^n} [(1 - x)^\alpha(1 + x)^\beta(1 - x^2)^n]$$

$$L_n^\alpha(x) = \frac{e^x x^{-\alpha}}{n!} \frac{d^n}{dx^n} (e^{-x} x^{n+\alpha})$$

$$H_n(x) = (-1)^n e^{x^2/2} \frac{d^n}{dx^n} e^{-x^2/2} .$$

The first of these yields the particular results

$$P_n(x) = \frac{(-1)^n}{2^n n!} \frac{d^n}{dx^n} (1 - x^2)^n$$

$$T_n(x) = \frac{(-1)^n 2^n n!}{(2n)!} \sqrt{1 - x^2} \frac{d^n}{dx^n} [(1 - x^2)^{n-1/2}] .$$

It is not immediately obvious that the above expressions are polynomials, but this can be shown by Leibniz' rule.* Each of these expressions can be written in the general form

$$\phi_n(x) = \frac{1}{w(x)} \frac{d^n}{dx^n} w(x) u^n(x),$$

where $w(x)$ and $u(x)$ are readily interpreted for each case. To show that these expressions are really orthogonal polynomials with weight function $w(x)$ it is sufficient to show that

$$\int_a^b w(x) \phi_N(x) x^i \, dx = 0, \qquad i = 0, 1, 2, \cdots, N - 1.$$

---

* See note 2 in the appendix to Chapter 1.

We now consider the integral

$$\int_a^b x^i \frac{d^n}{dx^n} w(x) \, u^n(x) \, dx$$

and perform n integrations by parts, which leads to

$$\int_a^b w(x) \, u^n(x) \frac{d^n}{dx^n} x^i \, dx,$$

but if n exceeds i the integrand vanishes, which proves the orthogonality.

Formulas of the type discussed in this section are generally called Rodrigues' formulas.

10. Generating Functions

The Rodrigues formulas are very convenient for the derivation of various types of generating functions. A generating function is a series of the type

$$\sum_{n=0}^{\infty} a_n \phi_n(x) t^n$$

and therefore a function of two variables t and x. For example, if we wish to evaluate the series

$$\sum_{n=0}^{\infty} P_n(x) t^n$$

we replace $P_n(x)$ by the Rodrigues formulas and use the Cauchy integral theorem.* Then

$$P_n(x) = \frac{(-1)^n}{2^n n!} \frac{d^n}{dx^n} (1 - x^2)^n = \frac{(-1)^n}{2^n} \frac{1}{2\pi i} \int_c \frac{(1 - z^2)^n}{(z - x)^{n+1}} \, dz \,.$$

Inserting this expression in the above summation and interchanging summation and integration, we obtain

$$\frac{1}{2\pi i} \int_c \frac{dz}{z - x} \sum_{n=0}^{\infty} \frac{(-1)^n}{2^n} t^n \left(\frac{1 - z^2}{z - x}\right)^n.$$

The resulting series is a simple geometric series, which is readily summed. We then obtain the integral

$$-\frac{1}{2\pi i} \int_c \frac{2}{t} \frac{dz}{z^2 - \frac{2}{t} z - \left(1 - \frac{2}{t} x\right)}.$$

* See note 3 in the appendix to Chapter 1.

To evaluate this integral we use the standard residue integration technique. The denominator has two roots—namely,

$$z = \frac{1}{t} \pm \sqrt{\frac{1}{t^2} - \frac{2}{t}x + 1},$$

but only the root corresponding to the minus sign is near the point x. The integration is carried out over a path surrounding x so that the value of the integral is given by

$$-\frac{2}{t} \lim_{z \to \frac{1}{t} - \sqrt{\frac{1}{t^2} - \frac{2}{t}x + 1}} \frac{z - \left(\frac{1}{t} - \sqrt{\frac{1}{t^2} - \frac{2}{t}x + 1}\right)}{z^2 - \frac{2}{t}z - \left(1 - \frac{2}{t}x\right)}$$

$$= \frac{1}{\sqrt{1 - 2xt + t^2}}.$$

Thus we have found the generating function

$$\frac{1}{\sqrt{1 - 2xt + t^2}} = \sum_{n=0}^{\infty} P_n(x)t^n.$$

The same method could be applied to the Tchebichef polynomials, but we will demonstrate another method of constructing generating functions by use of the recursion formula (Sec. 6). Suppose we wish to determine

$$G(x, t) = 1 + 2\sum_{1}^{\infty} T_n(x)t^n.$$

We multiply the recursion formula by t^n and sum over n. Then

$$\sum_{1}^{\infty} t^n T_{n+1}(x) - 2x\sum_{1}^{\infty} t^n T_n(x) + \sum_{1}^{\infty} t^n T_{n-1}(x) = 0.$$

Now we observe that

$$\sum_{1}^{\infty} t^n T_{n+1}(x) = \frac{1}{t}\left[\frac{G(x, t) - 1}{2} - tT_1(x)\right]$$

$$\sum_{1}^{\infty} t^n T_n(x) = \frac{G(x, t) - 1}{2}$$

$$\sum_{1}^{\infty} t^n T_{n-1}(x) = t\frac{G(x, t) + 1}{2}.$$

If we replace $T_1(x)$ in the first of these equations by its explicit form—namely, x,—and enter these terms in the above equation and solve for G algebraically we find that

$$G(x, t) = \frac{1 - t^2}{1 - 2xt + t^2} = 1 + 2 \sum_1^\infty T_n(x)t^n.$$

To construct the generating function of the Laguerre polynomials we return to our former method.

$$\sum_0^\infty L_n^\alpha(x)t^n = \sum_0^\infty t^n \frac{e^x x^{-\alpha}}{n!} \frac{d^n}{dx^n} e^{-x} x^\alpha x^n$$

$$= \sum_0^\infty t^n e^x x^{-\alpha} \frac{1}{2\pi i} \int_c \frac{e^{-\zeta} \zeta^{n+\alpha}}{(\zeta - x)^{n+1}} d\zeta .$$

By interchanging summation and integration and then summing the resultant geometric series we obtain

$$e^x x^{-\alpha} \frac{1}{2\pi i} \int_c \frac{e^{-\zeta} \zeta^\alpha d\zeta}{\zeta(1 - t) - x} .$$

We see that the integrand has a simple pole at $\zeta = \dfrac{x}{1 - t}$, and by a residue evaluation we see that

$$\sum_0^\infty L_n^\alpha(x)t^n = \frac{e^{-xt/(1-t)}}{(1 - t)^{\alpha+1}} .$$

The same method shows that

$$\sum_0^\infty H_n(x)\frac{t^n}{n!} = e^{tx-t^2/2} .$$

It should be noted that with any given family of functions one can associate several generating functions. Thus one can show by the same methods that

$$\sum_0^\infty L_n^{(\alpha-n)}(x)t^n = (1 + t)^\alpha e^{-xt}$$

and

$$\sum_0^\infty \frac{L_n^{(\alpha)}(x)t^n}{(n + \alpha)!} = e^t(xt)^{-\alpha/2} J_\alpha(2 \sqrt{tx}),$$

where $J_\alpha(z)$ denotes a Bessel function, which will be discussed in later chapters.

Furthermore one can use these generating functions as definitions of the corresponding functions. Just as we derived the generating function of the Tchebichef polynomials from the recursion formula, we could have worked backward and found the recursion formula from the generating function.

Similarly, all other properties of these can be derived. For example, one can define the Bessel functions by means of the generating function

$$e^{x/2(t-1/t)} = \sum_{-\infty}^{\infty} t^n J_n(x),$$

which can be used to derive the above generating function of the Laguerre polynomials. As an illustration we take the case $\alpha = 0$, and find that

$$\sum_0^{\infty} \frac{L_n^{(0)}(x)t^n}{n!} = e^x \frac{1}{2\pi i} \int_c \frac{e^{-\xi}d\zeta}{\zeta - x} \sum_0^{\infty} \frac{\left(\dfrac{t\zeta}{\zeta - x}\right)^n}{n!}.$$

The summation is readily summed as an exponential function and the variable of integration is replaced by

$$\zeta = x - \sqrt{tx}\, u.$$

The integral becomes now

$$\frac{e^t}{2\pi i} \int_c \frac{du}{u} e^{(2\sqrt{xt}/2)(u-1/u)} = \frac{e^t}{2\pi i} \int_c \frac{du}{u} \sum_{-\infty}^{\infty} u^n J_n(2\sqrt{xt}) = e^t J_0(2\sqrt{xt})$$

so that

$$\sum_{n=0}^{\infty} \frac{L_n^{(0)}(x)t^n}{n!} = e^t J_0(2\sqrt{tx}) .$$

11. Normalization

We have seen that

$$\int_a^b w(x)\, \phi_n(x)\, \phi_m(x)\, dx = 0, \qquad n \neq m,$$

but we have said nothing about the case $n = m$. Evidently the integral cannot vanish in that case. We can evaluate these integrals by use of the generating functions. For example, we square the generating function of the Legendre polynomials (Sec. 10) and integrate over the interval $(-1, 1)$. Thus

$$\int_{-1}^1 \frac{dx}{1 - 2xt + t^2} = \sum_0^{\infty} t^{2n} \int_{-1}^1 P_n^2(x)\, dx.$$

The integral on the left is $\dfrac{1}{t} \ln \dfrac{1+t}{1-t}$, which is then expanded in a Taylor series so that

$$\sum_0^{\infty} \frac{2t^{2n}}{2n + 1} = \sum_0^{\infty} t^{2n} \int_{-1}^1 P_n^2(x)\, dx.$$

We see that

$$\int_{-1}^{1} P_n^2(x)\, dx = \frac{2}{2n+1}.$$

Similarly, we can show that

$$\int_{-1}^{1} \frac{T_n^2(x)}{\sqrt{1-x^2}}\, dx = \frac{\pi}{2}, \qquad n \neq 0$$

$$= \pi, \qquad n = 0$$

$$\int_{0}^{\infty} e^{-x} x^{\alpha} \left[L_n^{(\alpha)}(x) \right]^2 dx = \frac{(n+\alpha)!}{n!}, \qquad \alpha > -1$$

$$\int_{-\infty}^{\infty} e^{-x^2/2} H_n^2(x)\, dx = \sqrt{2\pi}\, n!\,.$$

12. Applications to Quadrature Problems

Among the many applications of these functions, one of the most important is the approximation of functions. Suppose $p(x)$ is an arbitrary polynomial of degree $n-1$ and let $x_1, x_2, \cdots, x_n$ denote the n zeros of some orthogonal polynomial $\phi_n(x)$. Then

$$F(x) = \sum_{i=1}^{n} p(x_i)\, \frac{\phi_n(x)}{\phi_n'(x_i)\,(x-x_i)}$$

is a polynomial of degree $n-1$, which coincides with $p(x)$ at the n points $x_1, \cdots, x_n$, and therefore is identically equal to $p(x)$. Of course, if $p(x)$ is of higher degree, $F(x)$ cannot represent $p(x)$ exactly, but only approximately. This formula is usually known as Lagrange's interpolation formula. But we will show that even if $p(x)$ is a polynomial of degree as high as $2n-1$, it is still true that

$$\int_a^b w(x)\, F(x)\, dx = \int_a^b w(x)\, p(x)\, dx,$$

where $w(x)$ is the weight function associated with $\phi_n(x)$. To do so we observe that $p(x) - F(x)$ is of degree at most $2n-1$ and certainly has among its zeros those of $\phi_n(x)$ since

$$p(x_i) = F(x_i) \qquad \text{for } \phi_n(x_i) = 0.$$

Therefore

$$p(x) - F(x) = \phi_n(x)\, r(x),$$

where $r(x)$ has at most degree $n-1$. Then

$$\int_a^b w(x)\, p(x)\, dx - \int_a^b w(x)\, F(x)\, dx = \int_a^b w(x)\, \phi_n(x)\, r(x)\, dx = 0$$

since $\phi_n(x)$ is orthogonal to every polynomial of lower degree. This proves the assertion.

It now follows that

$$\int_a^b w(x)\, p(x)\, dx = \sum_{i=1}^n p(x_i) \int_a^b w(x)\, \frac{\phi_n(x)}{\phi_n'(x_i)\,(x - x_i)}\, dx\ .$$

It is evident that

$$\lambda_i = \int_a^b w(x)\, \frac{\phi_n(x)}{\phi_n'(x_i)\,(x - x_i)}\, dx$$

is independent of $p(x)$. These numbers are called the Christoffel numbers, and we can write

$$\int_a^b w(x)\, p(x)\, dx = \sum_1^n p(x_i)\, \lambda_i.$$

This formula says that if $p(x)$ is a polynomial of at most degree $2n - 1$, then the integral can be evaluated if one knows the value of $p(x)$ at no more than n points. This process can be used to evaluate integrals approximately when $p(x)$ is not a polynomial of at most degree $2n - 1$. This formula is often called Gauss' quadrature formula, after Gauss, who derived it for the special case $w(x) = 1$, when the $\phi_n(x)$ are the Legendre polynomials.

13. Expansion Theorems

Among the important results associated with orthogonal polynomials are the expansions of arbitrary functions. We will now assume that $\phi_N(x)$ is a member of an orthonormal family and we will try to determine coefficients α_i so that

$$E_n = \int_a^b w(x) \left[f(x) - \sum_{i=0}^n \alpha_i\, \phi_i(x) \right]^2 dx$$

is minimized.

We introduce the terms f_i defined by

$$f_i = \int_a^b w(x)\, f(x)\, \phi_i(x)\, dx$$

and let

$$\alpha_i = f_i + \epsilon_i.$$

Then

$$E_n = \int_a^b w(x)\, f^2(x)\, dx - 2 \sum_{i=0}^n (f_i + \epsilon_i) \int_a^b w(x)\, f(x)\, \phi_i(x)\, dx$$

$$+ \sum_{i=0}^n (f_i + \epsilon_i)^2 \int_a^b w(x)\, \phi_i^2(x)\, dx.$$

Since the $\phi_i(x)$ are orthonormal, that is,

$$\int_a^b w(x)\,\phi_i^2(x)\,dx = 1, \qquad i = 0, 1, 2, \cdots,$$

we find that

$$E_n = \int_a^b w(x)\,f^2(x)\,dx - \sum_{i=0}^n f_i^2 + \sum_{i=0}^u \epsilon_i^2.$$

We see that to minimize E_n it is necessary that all $\epsilon_i = 0$, that is, $\alpha_i = f_i$. We will now show that if $f(x)$ is a continuous function then

$$\lim_{n \to \infty} E_n = 0,$$

which then implies Parseval's formula,

$$\sum_{i=0}^\infty f_i^2 = \int_a^b w(x)\,f^2(x)\,dx.$$

The proof is based on Weierstrass's theorem,* which states that for every continuous function $f(x)$, defined in some finite interval $[a, b]$, and an arbitrary tolerance ϵ one can find a polynomial $p(x)$ so that

$$|f(x) - p(x)| \le \epsilon \qquad \text{for } x \text{ in } [a, b].$$

To show that E_n approaches zero, it is sufficient to show that for any given δ we can find an $N(\delta)$ so that

$$E_n < \delta \qquad \text{for all } n > N(\delta).$$

We now find a polynomial $p(x)$ of degree n so that

$$|f(x) - p(x)| \le \sqrt{\frac{\delta}{\int_a^b w(x)\,dx}} \qquad \begin{array}{l} \text{for } x \text{ in } [a, b] \\ \text{and } n > N(\delta), \end{array}$$

and we can certainly express $p(x)$ in a finite series of orthogonal polynomials. We define $r(x)$ by

$$f(x) = p(x) + \sqrt{\frac{\delta}{\int_a^b w(x)\,dx}}\,r(x),$$

where evidently $|r(x)| \le 1$.
Let

$$p(x) = \sum_{i=0}^m \alpha_i\,\phi_i(x),$$

where the number of terms required in the summation is $m + 1$, where m need not equal n.

---

* See note 4 in the appendix to Chapter 1.

Then

$$\left| E_n \right| = \left| \int_a^b w(x) \frac{\delta}{\int_a^b w(x)\, dx}\, r(x)\, dx \right| \le \delta.$$

The above proof applies only to finite intervals but can be modified to apply to infinite intervals as well.

One interesting consequence of this statement is that the best approximation to zero of the form $x^n + \cdots$ must be $k\phi_n(x)$. This follows from the fact that

$$\int_a^b w(x)\, p^2(x)\, dx,$$

where $p(x)$ is a polynomial of degree n with leading coefficient unity, is minimized by $p(x) = k\phi_n(x)$.

What we have shown, therefore, is that we can expand arbitrary continuous functions in Fourier-type series. That is,

$$f(x) = \sum_{i=0}^{\infty} f_i\, \phi_i(x)$$

$$f_i = \int_a^b w(x)\, f(x)\, \phi_i(x)\, dx, \qquad \int_a^b w(x)\, \phi_i^2(x)\, dx = 1;$$

where $\lim_{n\to\infty} E_n = \lim_{n\to\infty} \int_a^b w(x) \left[f(x) - \sum_{i=0}^{n} f_i\, \phi_i(x) \right]^2 dx = 0.$

Convergence of this type is called convergence in the mean. Families of orthonormal functions of this type are called complete. As a matter of fact, one can show that the conditions imposed on $f(x)$ can be considerably weakened to a point where all that is required is that

$$\int_a^b w(x)\, f^2(x)\, dx$$

exists. Conversely, an infinite set of $\{f_i\}$ such that $\sum_0^{\infty} f_i^2$ exists defines a function of this type by the expansion.

14. Relationship to Hypergeometric Functions

The differential equation

$$x\,(1 - x)y'' + \left[c - (a + b + 1)x \right] y' - aby = 0$$

is called the hypergeometric equation. If one seeks a power series solution about the point $x = 0$ one finds that the solution has the form

$$_2F_1(a, b; c; x) = \sum_{n=0}^{\infty} \frac{(a)_n (b)_n}{(c_n)} \frac{x^n}{n!},$$

where

$$(a)_n = a(a + 1) \cdots (a + n - 1).$$

Many of the special functions that arise in mathematical physics are special cases of this class of functions. Thus one can readily show that the Jacobi polynomials can be expressed as

$$P_n^{(\alpha,\beta)}(x) = \binom{n+\alpha}{n} {}_2F_1\left(-n, n+\alpha+\beta+1; \alpha+1; \frac{1-x}{2}\right).^*$$

Then we find that

$$P_n(x) = {}_2F_1\left(-n, n+1; 1; \frac{1-x}{2}\right)$$

$$T_n(x) = {}_2F_1\left(-n, n; \frac{1}{2}; \frac{1-x}{2}\right).$$

If one replaces the variable x by z/b in the hypergeometric equation and allows b to become infinite, the resultant equation becomes

$$zy'' + (c-z)y' - ay = 0$$

and the solution of this equation becomes

$$_1F_1(a; c; z) = \sum_{n=0}^{\infty} \frac{(a)_n}{(c_n)} \frac{z^n}{n!}.$$

This equation is called the confluent hypergeometric equation. One can show that

$$L_n^{(\alpha)}(x) = \frac{(\alpha+1)_n}{n!} {}_1F_1(-n; \alpha+1; x)$$

$$H_{2n}(x) = \frac{(-1)^n(2n)!}{2^n n!} {}_1F_1\left(-n; \frac{1}{2}; \frac{x^2}{2}\right)$$

$$H_{2n+1}(x) = \frac{(-1)^n(2n+1)!}{2^n n!} x {}_1F_1\left(-n; \frac{3}{2}; \frac{x^2}{2}\right).$$

In many books on special functions the hypergeometric functions are treated in detail and at great length. Although this treatment is useful and rewarding, such a study would carry us too far afield from our immediate goal.

Appendix

Note 1. We wish to show that the system of equations

$$\int_a^b w(x) x^i \phi_N(x)\, dx = 0, \qquad i = 0, 1, 2, \cdots, N-1$$

determines the coefficients in $\phi_N(x)$ to within an arbitrary multiplier. We now let

$$\phi_N(x) = \alpha_N x^N + \alpha_{N-1} x^{N-1} + \cdots + \alpha_1 x + \alpha_0.$$

---

* See note 5 in the appendix to Chapter 1.

We insert that in the integral and construct the following system of equations

$$\alpha_{N-1} \int_a^b w(x) \, x^{i+N-1} \, dx + \alpha_{N-2} \int_a^b w(x) \, x^{i+N-2} \, dx + \cdots + \alpha_0 \int_a^b w(x) \, x^i \, dx$$

$$= - \alpha_N \int_a^b w(x) \, x^{N+i} \, dx$$

$$i = 0, 1, 2, \cdots, N - 1.$$

To show that these N equations determine the N constants α_{N-1}, α_{N-2}, $\cdots$, α_0 uniquely in terms of α_N it is necessary to show that the determinant of this system does not vanish. To do so we consider the quadratic form in the $N - 1$ variables $u_0, u_1, \cdots, u_{N-1}$

$$D(u_0, u_1, \cdots, u_{N-1}) = \int_a^b w(x) \big[u_0 + u_1 x + \cdots + u_{N-1} x^{N-1} \big]^2 \, dx.$$

Evidently D is nonnegative and can vanish only if all u_i vanish. Thus D has a minimum at $u_i = 0$ for $i = 0, 1, 2, \cdots, N - 1$. It is therefore necessary that the system of equations

$$\frac{\partial D}{\partial u_i} = 2 \int_a^b w(x) \, x^i \Big[u_0 + u_1 x \cdots + u_{N-1} x^{N-1} \Big] \, dx = 0$$

$$i = 0, 1, 2, \cdots, N - 1$$

have a unique solution,—namely, $u_i = 0$ for $i = 0, 1, 2, \cdots, N - 1$. The determinant of this system thus cannot vanish; otherwise we could find another solution for which some $u_i \neq 0$, which is impossible for the given function D. But the determinant of this system is identical to the one of the system determining the coefficients for $\phi_N(x)$. Thus $\alpha_0, \alpha_1, \cdots, \alpha_{N-1}$ are uniquely determined in terms of α_N.

Note 2. Leibniz' rule states that

$$\frac{d^n}{dx^n} f(x) \times g(x) = \sum_{k=0}^{n} \frac{n!}{k!(n-k)!} f^{(k)}(x) \, g^{(n-k)}(x).$$

If one uses symbolical notation—that is, D for differentiation with respect to x, D_f for differentiation with respect to x—but applied only to $f(x)$ and similarly for $g(x)$ one can rewrite the above formula as

$$D^n f(x) g(x) = (D_f + D_g)^n f(x) g(x).$$

The proof can be furnished readily by mathematical induction.

Note 3. The Cauchy integral theorem states that if $f(z)$ is analytic in some domain and on its boundary C, and z is an interior point, then

$$\frac{1}{2\pi i} \int_c \frac{f(\zeta)}{\zeta - z} \, d\zeta = f(z).$$

By successive differentiations with respect to z, we can derive the result that

$$\frac{n!}{2\pi i} \int_c \frac{f(\zeta)}{(\zeta - z)^{n+1}} \, d\zeta = \frac{d^n}{dz^n} f(z).$$

Note 4. We will prove Weierstrass' theorem, which states that if $f(x)$ is continuous in the closed interval $[a, b]$ it can be approximated to an arbitrary degree of closeness by polynomials. More precisely, given an ϵ we can find a polynomial $p(x)$ so that

$$|f(x) - p(x)| < \epsilon \qquad \text{for } x \text{ in } [a, b].$$

In particular, we will show that the Bernstein polynomials approximate $f(x)$—that is,

$$\lim_{n \to \infty} \sum_{p=0}^{n} \binom{n}{p} f\left(\frac{p}{n}\right) x^p (1 - x)^{n-p} = f(x).$$

The expression $\binom{n}{p} = \dfrac{n!}{p!(n - p)!}$ is the general binomial coefficient and the interval $[a, b]$ was taken to be $[0, 1]$. This can always be accomplished by a suitable change of variable.

Before proceeding to the general proof we will indicate a statistical interpretation of this statement. Let us subdivide the interval $[0, 1]$ into two subintervals, $[0, x]$ and $[x, 1]$. We now conceive the following game: We pick n numbers at random from $[0, 1]$. If we pick p numbers from $[0, x]$ and $n - p$ from $[x, 1]$ then the payoff is $f\left(\dfrac{p}{n}\right)$. Evidently the probability of this event is

$$\binom{n}{p} x^p (1 - x)^{n-p}$$

and the expectation of the game is

$$\sum_{p=0}^{n} \binom{n}{p} x^p (1 - x)^{n-p} f\left(\frac{p}{n}\right).$$

If n is large the most probable value of p is nx. In that case $f\left(\dfrac{p}{n}\right)$ is $f(x)$. Therefore if n is large the expectation is $f(x)$.

We will now prove the statement rigorously, without recourse to intuitive notions. First we observe that

$$(x + y)^n = \sum_{p=0}^{n} \binom{n}{p} x^p y^{n-p};$$

then by differentiation with respect to x and multiplication by x

$$nx(x + y)^{n-1} = \sum_{p=0}^{n} \binom{n}{p} p \, x^p y^{n-p}.$$

A repetition of this process shows that

$$nx(x + y)^{n-1} + n(n - 1) x^2(x + y)^{n-1} = \sum_{p=0}^{n} \binom{n}{p} p^2 \, x^p \, y^{n-p}.$$

After replacing y by $1 - x$, we can put these three statements into the form

$$\sum_{p=0}^{n} \binom{n}{p} x^p \, (1 - x)^{n-p} = 1$$

$$\sum_{p=0}^{n} \binom{n}{p} \left(\frac{p}{n}\right) x^p \, (1 - x)^{n-p} = x$$

$$\sum_{p=0}^{n} \binom{n}{p} \left(\frac{p}{n}\right)^2 x^p \, (1 - x)^{n-p} = x^2 + \frac{x(1 - x)}{n}.$$

These statements are particular cases of the general formula for $f(x) = 1$, $f(x) = x$, and $f(x) = x^2$ respectiviely.

Secondly we observe that

$$\sum_{|p - nx| > n\epsilon} \binom{n}{p} x^p \, (1 - x)^{n-p} < \sum_{|p - nx| > n\epsilon} \left(\frac{p - nx}{n\epsilon}\right)^2 \binom{n}{p} x^p \, (1 - x)^{n-p}$$

$$< \sum_{p=0}^{n} \left(\frac{p - nx}{n\epsilon}\right)^2 \binom{n}{p} x^p \, (1 - x)^{n-p}$$

$$= \frac{1}{n^2 \epsilon^2} \sum_{p=0}^{n} (p^2 - 2pnx + n^2x^2) \binom{n}{p} x^p \, (1 - x)^{n-p} = \frac{x(1 - x)}{n\epsilon^2}.$$

In the first summation we do not sum over all p but only those for which

$$n \geq p > nx + n\epsilon, \qquad 0 \leq p < nx - n\epsilon;$$

that is, we exclude those values of p near nx. The first inequality follows from the fact that we replace a coefficient of 1 by $\left(\dfrac{p - nx}{n\epsilon}\right)^2$, which is larger for the p's under consideration. The second inequality follows from the fact that we have introduced more nonnegative terms into the summation. The remainder follows from the special results found above. We now proceed to the proof of the general results.

We wish to show that

$$\left| f(x) - \sum_{0}^{n} \binom{n}{p} f\left(\frac{p}{n}\right) x^p(1 - x)^{n-p} \right| < \delta$$

$$\text{for } n > N(\delta);$$

that is, for suitable choices of n we can fit $f(x)$ within any required tolerance.

Since $f(x)$ is continuous in the interval $[0, 1]$ and therefore also bounded by some constant M we can say that

$$\left| f(x) - f\left(\frac{p}{n}\right) \right| < \frac{\delta}{2} \quad \text{for} \ \left| x - \left(\frac{p}{n}\right) \right| < \epsilon(\delta)$$

and

$$\left| f(x) - f\left(\frac{p}{n}\right) \right| < 2M \ \text{for all} \ x \ \text{in} \ [0, 1].$$

Now

$$\left| f(x) - \sum_0^n \binom{n}{p} f\left(\frac{p}{n}\right) x^p (1-x)^{n-p} \right|$$

$$= \left| \sum_0^n \binom{n}{p} \left[f(x) - f\left(\frac{p}{n}\right) \right] x^p (1-x)^{n-p} \right|$$

$$\leq \sum_{|p - nx| \leq n\epsilon} \binom{n}{p} \left| f(x) - f\left(\frac{p}{n}\right) \right| x^p (1-x)^{n-p}$$

$$+ \sum_{|p - nx| > n\epsilon} \binom{n}{p} \left| f(x) - f\left(\frac{p}{n}\right) \right| x^p (1-x)^{n-p}.$$

Let us now inspect each of the last two terms individually.

$$\sum_{|p - nx| \leq n\epsilon} \binom{n}{p} \left| f(x) - f\left(\frac{p}{n}\right) \right| x^p (1-x)^{n-p} \leq \frac{\delta}{2} \sum_{|p - nx| \leq n\epsilon} \binom{n}{p} x^p (1-x)^{n-p} \leq \frac{\delta}{2}.$$

The first follows from the hypothesis on $f(x) - f\left(\frac{p}{n}\right)$ in the interval $|p - nx| \leq n\epsilon$, and the second from the fact that the summation is part of the expansion $[x + (1 - x)]^n$.

$$\sum_{|p - nx| > n\epsilon} \binom{n}{p} \left| f(x) - f\left(\frac{p}{n}\right) \right| x^p (1-x)^{n-p}$$

$$< 2M \sum_{|p - nx| > n\epsilon} \binom{n}{p} x^p (1-x)^{n-p} \leq \frac{2Mx(1-x)}{n\epsilon^2} < \frac{\delta}{2}.$$

The first part follows since $f(x)$ is a bounded function, and the second from the previous result. Recognizing that

$$x(1 - x) \leq \tfrac{1}{4} \quad \text{for} \ x \ \text{in} \ \left[0, 1\right]$$

and choosing $n > \dfrac{M}{\delta \epsilon^2}$ leads to the last step. We combine all these results and see that

$$\left| f(x) - \sum_{0}^{n} \binom{n}{p} f\left(\frac{p}{n}\right) x^p (1-x)^{n-p} \right| < \delta$$

$$\text{for } n > \frac{M}{\delta \epsilon^2(\delta)},$$

which we set out to prove.

Note 5. The symbol

$$\binom{n+\alpha}{n}$$

is a binomial coefficient that is commonly defined by

$$\frac{(n+\alpha)!}{n!\,\alpha!} = \frac{(n+\alpha)(n+\alpha-1)\cdots(\alpha+1)}{n!}.$$

Although the expression on the left is, as yet, defined only for integral values, the expression on the right has meaning even if α is not an integer.

In general, one can extend the meaning of $n!$ to nonintegral values by realizing that

$$n! = \int_0^\infty e^{-t} t^n \, dt.$$

This integral exists for all $n > -1$ and one can extend the meaning of $n!$ by means of it. Usually one then introduces the Gamma function defined by

$$\Gamma(n+1) = \int_0^\infty e^{-t} t^n \, dt,$$

which defines the function for all $n > -1$. For integral values of n we evidently have

$$\Gamma(n+1) = n!.$$

This function does not satisfy a differential equation, but is usually considered as a special function. Its value is that with its help many of the functions that depend on integral parameters can be extended to arbitrary parameters. Thus, for example, we can see that the value of the integral

$$\int_0^\infty e^{-x} x^\alpha \left[L_n^{(\alpha)}(x) \right]^2 dx = \frac{(n+\alpha)!}{n!} = \frac{\Gamma(n+\alpha+1)}{n!}$$

can be extended from integral α to arbitrary α by the introduction of a Gamma function.

Exercises

1. Show that

$$T_n(x) = \cos(n \cos^{-1} x).$$

2. Show that if $x_1, x_2, \cdots, x_n$ are the zeros of $T_n(x)$ and $f(x)$ is a polynomial of degree $n-1$, then

$$f(x) = \frac{1}{n} \sum_{k=1}^{n} (-1)^{k-1} \sqrt{1 - x_k^2} f(x_k) \frac{T_n(x)}{x - x_k}.$$

3. Show that

$$H_n(x) = \frac{1}{\sqrt{2\pi}} \int_{-\infty}^{\infty} (x + it)^n e^{-t^2/2} \, dt.$$

4. Show that

$$\sum_{n=0}^{\infty} H_n(x) H_n(y) \frac{t^n}{n!} = \frac{1}{\sqrt{1 - t^2}} \exp\left[\frac{2xyt - t^2(x^2 + y^2)}{2(1 - t^2)}\right].$$

5. Show that

$$\sum_{m=0}^{n} \binom{n}{m} H_{n-m}(\sqrt{2t}) H_m(\sqrt{2\tau}) = 2^{n/2} H_n(t + \tau).$$

6. Show that

$$\frac{d}{dx} L_{n+1}^{(\alpha)}(x) = -L_n^{(\alpha+1)}(x).$$

7. Show that

$$P_n(x) = \sqrt{\frac{2}{\pi}} \frac{1}{n!} \int_0^{\infty} e^{-t^2/2} t^n H_n(xt) \, dt.$$

8. Show that

$$\lim_{\beta \to \infty} P_n^{(\alpha,\beta)} \left(1 - \frac{2t}{\beta}\right) = L_n^\alpha(t).$$

9. Show that

$$H_{2n}(t) = \frac{(-)^n}{1 \times 3 \cdots (2n-1)} L_n^{(-1/2)}\left(\frac{t^2}{2}\right)$$

$$H_{2n+1}(t) = \frac{(-)^{n+1}}{1 \times 3 \cdots (2n+1)} L_n^{(1/2)}\left(\frac{t^2}{2}\right)$$

for $n = 0, 1, 2, \cdots$.

10. Show that every orthogonal polynomial can be represented in the form

$$\phi_n(x) = K \begin{vmatrix} C_0 & C_1 & \cdots & C_n \\ C_1 & C_2 & \cdots & C_{n+1} \\ C_{n-1} & C_n & \cdots & C_{2n-1} \\ 1 & x & \cdots & x^n \end{vmatrix},$$

where $C_i = \int_a^b w(x) \, x^i \, dx$.

[2]

The Legendre Functions

1. Introduction

Among the greatest stimuli for the study of special functions were many of the problems that arose in mathematical physics. The three equations of fundamental importance that occur most frequently are

$$\Delta u = 0,$$

$$\alpha^2 \Delta u = u_t;$$

$$c^2 \Delta u = u_{tt}.$$

Here $u_t \equiv \dfrac{\partial u}{\partial t}$, $u_{tt} \equiv \dfrac{\partial^2 u}{\partial t^2}$, etc., t being a time dimension. The symbol Δ denotes the Laplacian operator, which has the form, when expressed in rectangular coordinates,

$$\Delta u = u_{xx} + u_{yy} + u_{zz};$$

in cylindrical coordinates,

$$\Delta u = u_{\rho\rho} + \frac{1}{\rho}u_\rho + \frac{1}{\rho^2}u_{\phi\phi} + u_{zz}$$

$$\rho = \sqrt{x^2 + y^2}$$

$$\phi = \tan^{-1}\frac{y}{x} \;;$$

and in spherical coordinates,

$$\Delta u = u_{rr} + \frac{2}{r}u_r + \frac{1}{r^2 \sin \theta}\frac{\partial}{\partial \theta}(\sin \theta \, u_\theta) + \frac{1}{r^2 \sin^2 \theta} u_{\phi\phi}$$

$$r = \sqrt{x^2 + y^2 + z^2}$$

$$\theta = \tan^{-1}\frac{\sqrt{x^2 + y^2}}{z}$$

$$\phi = \tan^{-1}\frac{y}{x} \,.$$

26

The first of the above-mentioned equations is known as Laplace's equation and is commonly associated with potential problems, such as gravitational and electrostatic potentials. The second equation is known as the heat-flow equation and arises in various diffusion processes; the parameter α^2 is commonly called the diffusivity and is a physical constant that depends on the properties of the material in which the diffusion process takes place. The last equation is called the wave equation, and as the name implies, governs wave phenomena; the parameter c has the dimension of velocity and represents the speed of propagation of the wave in the medium under consideration.

We will now examine Laplace's equation in greater detail. To do so we will operate in spherical coordinates and will apply the method of separation of variables. That is, we assume that u can be expressed in the form

$$u = R(r) \, P(\theta) \, E(\phi).$$

Inserting this expression in Laplace's equation and dividing by u we arrive at

$$\left[\frac{r^2 R''(r)}{R(r)} + \frac{2r R'(r)}{R(r)} \right] + \left[\frac{1}{\sin \theta} \frac{\frac{\partial}{\partial \theta} \sin \theta P'(\theta)}{P(\theta)} \right] + \frac{1}{\sin^2 \theta} \left[\frac{E''(\phi)}{E(\phi)} \right] = 0.$$

Since every bracketed expression is a function of a single variable, and the three variables r, θ, ϕ are independent, we see by a well-known argument that

$$\frac{E''(\phi)}{E(\phi)} = -m^2$$

$$\frac{1}{\sin \theta} \frac{\frac{d}{d\theta} \sin \theta \, P'(\theta)}{P(\theta)} - \frac{m^2}{\sin^2 \theta} = -n(n+1)$$

$$\frac{r^2 R''(r)}{R(r)} + \frac{2r R'(r)}{R(r)} = n(n+1).$$

The constants m and $n \, (n+1)$ are known as the separation constants; the form $n(n+1)$ is so chosen for convenience. The first and last of these differential equations are easily solved and we see that

$$E = c_1 e^{im\phi} + c_2 e^{-im\phi}$$

$$R = c_3 r^n + c_4 r^{-n-1}.$$

Since the function E should have period 2π we conclude that m must be an integer.

The second equation cannot be solved in terms of familiar functions. We first perform a change of independent variable by letting $\cos \theta = t$. The equation then takes the form

$$(1 - t^2) \frac{d^2 P}{dt^2} - 2t \frac{dP}{dt} + \left[n(n+1) - \frac{m^2}{1 - t^2} \right] P = 0.$$

We shall first concern ourselves with the case $m = 0$. In this case the equation has the form of Legendre's equation, which was discussed in Chapter 1. But there n was an integer, whereas here we have no reason as yet to suppose that n must be an integer. In view of the fact that $0 \leq \theta \leq \pi$, we see that $-1 \leq t \leq 1$. We expect the solution of the equation to be a regular function for $-1 \leq t \leq 1$. When n is an integer the solution is a polynomial, which is certainly regular. But when n is not a positive integer one can easily show, by assuming a power series solution, that the resultant series must diverge at $t = \pm 1$. We will therefore restrict ourselves to those cases where n is a positive integer. Nevertheless, it should be borne in mind that there are applications where more general cases must be considered. Furthermore, we are dealing with a second-order linear differential equation and therefore a second linearly independent solution exists, which we have so far ignored. Since this solution is also not regular for $-1 \leq t \leq 1$, we shall not deal with it. We will denote the general regular solution of the above equation by the symbol $P_n^m(t)$ and we see that $P_n^o(t) = P_n(t)$, the Legendre polynomial. The third equation

$$r^2 R'' + 2rR' - n(n + 1)R = 0$$

is of the Euler type and evidently has the general solution

$$R = c_1 r^n + \frac{c_2}{r^{n+1}}.$$

2. The Associated Legendre Function

We can relate the function $P_n^m(t)$, which is known as the associated Legendre function of the first kind, very simply to the Legendre polynomial. We replace $P_n^m(t)$ by $(1 - t^2)^{m/2} V(t)$ in the differential equation and thus find that $V(t)$ satisfies the equation

$$(1 - t^2)V'' - 2t(m + 1)V' + [n(n + 1) - m(m + 1)]V = 0.$$

If we take the Legendre equation

$$(1 - t^2)P_n'' - 2t\, P_n' + n(n + 1)P_n = 0$$

and differentiate this equation m times we find that

$$(1 - t^2)\frac{d^{m+2}}{dt^{m+2}} P_n - 2t(m + 1)\frac{d^{m+1}}{dt^{m+1}} P_n + \left[n(n + 1) - m(m + 1)\right]\frac{d^m}{dt^m} P_n = 0.$$

Comparing the last two differential equations we see that

$$P_n^m(t) = (-1)^m(1 - t^2)^{m/2}\frac{d^m}{dt^m} P_n(t).$$

The factor of $(-1)^m$ is inserted as a matter of convention.

3. Solutions of Laplace's Equation

We see that we can thus find solutions of Laplace's equation of the form

$$u = (c_1 e^{im\phi} + c_2 e^{-im\phi})(c_3 r^n + c_4 r^{-n-1}) P_n^m(\cos \theta).$$

The most basic solution of this form corresponds to the case $n = m = 0$; then

$$u = \frac{1}{r}.$$

It was first observed by J. C. Maxwell that we can derive all the other solutions we have so far found from this basic solution. It follows immediately from Laplace's equation that any derivative of a solution u, with respect to x, y, or z, is also a solution. Therefore

$$\frac{\partial}{\partial z} \frac{1}{r} = \frac{-z}{r^3}$$

must be a solution; in particular, it can be written in the form

$$\frac{\partial}{\partial z} \frac{1}{r} = -\frac{1}{r^2} P_1(\cos \theta)$$

since $P_1(\cos \theta) = \cos \theta = z/r$. If we perform n differentiations with respect to z we observe that

$$r^{n+1} \frac{\partial^n}{\partial z^n} \frac{1}{r} = F(z, r).$$

But both r and z have the dimensions of distance and the left side is dimensionless, so that the right side is also dimensionless and can be represented as some function of z/r or $\cos \theta$. Then

$$\frac{\partial^n}{\partial z^n} \frac{1}{r} = \frac{f(\cos \theta)}{r^{n+1}}$$

and a comparison with the basic solution obtained shows that

$$f(\cos \theta) = c\, P_n(\cos \theta).$$

Similarly, we see that

$$\left(\frac{\partial}{\partial x} + i\frac{\partial}{\partial y}\right) \frac{1}{r} = -\frac{1}{r^3}(x + iy) = -\frac{\sin \theta \, e^{i\phi}}{r^2};$$

which is of the form

$$\frac{P_1^1(\cos \theta) \, e^{i\phi}}{r^2}.$$

By an argument similar to the previous one we see that

$$\left(\frac{\partial}{\partial x} + i\frac{\partial}{\partial y}\right)^n \frac{1}{r} = \frac{c\, P_n^n(\cos \theta) \, e^{in\phi}}{r^{n+1}}$$

or more generally

$$\left(\frac{\partial}{\partial z}\right)^{n-m} \left(\frac{\partial}{\partial x} + i\frac{\partial}{\partial y}\right)^{m} \frac{1}{r} = \frac{c\, e^{im\phi}\, P_n^m(\cos\theta)}{r^{n+1}}$$

$$m = 0, 1, 2, \cdots, n.$$

The constant of proportionality c is not fully determined since it depends strongly on the exact definition of the Legendre functions. By comparing the highest order terms one can now show that

$$\left(\frac{\partial}{\partial z}\right)^{n-m} \left(\frac{\partial}{\partial x} + i\frac{\partial}{\partial y}\right)^{m} \frac{1}{r} = \frac{(-)^{n-m}(n-m)!}{r^{n+1}}\, e^{im\phi}\, P_n^m(\cos\theta)$$

$$m = 0, 1, 2, \cdots, n.$$

The potential, due to a point charge placed at $x = 0$, $y = 0$, $z = 1$, at an arbitrary point in space is given by $1/R$, the reciprocal of the distance from the point of observation to the charge. Expressing R in polar coordinates we find that

$$\frac{1}{R} = \frac{1}{\sqrt{1 - 2r\cos\theta + r^2}}$$

where r and θ are the spherical coordinates of the point of observation. If we expand this function in a power series in r we find that

$$\frac{1}{\sqrt{1 - 2r\cos\theta + r^2}} = \sum_{0}^{\infty} r^n P_n(\cos\theta) \qquad |r| < 1$$

$$= \sum_{0}^{\infty} \frac{P_n(\cos\theta)}{r^{n+1}} \qquad |r| > 1.$$

These expansions follow immediately if we recognize the left side as the generating function of the Legendre polynomials, which was discussed in Chapter 1.

4. Integral Representations

One of the most basic integral representations of the Legendre polynomials follows from Rodrigues' formula. We saw in Chapter 1 that

$$P_n(t) = \frac{1}{2^n n!} \left(\frac{d}{dt}\right)^n (t^2 - 1)^n;$$

and using the formula

$$\left(\frac{d}{d\zeta}\right)^n f(\zeta) = \frac{n!}{2\pi i} \int_c \frac{f(z)}{(z - \zeta)^{n+1}}\, dz,$$

where c is a contour surrounding the point $z = \zeta$, we obtain

$$P_n(t) = \frac{2^{-n}}{2\pi i} \int_c \frac{(z^2 - 1)^n}{(z - t)^{n+1}} \, dz.$$

More generally, since

$$P_n^m(t) = (-)^m \, (1 - t^2)^{m/2} \left(\frac{d}{dt}\right)^m P_n(t)$$

we obtain the representation

$$P_n^m(t) = \frac{(-)^m 2^{-n}}{2\pi i} \frac{(n + m)!}{n!} (1 - t^2)^{m/2} \int_c \frac{(z^2 - 1)^n}{(z - t)^{n+m+1}} \, dz.$$

In many applications it is more convenient to deal with a definite integral over a real interval. We now choose as our contour of integration a circle centered at the point $z = t$, let $t = \cos \theta$, and

$$z = \cos \theta + i \sin \theta \, e^{i\psi},$$

where ψ will be the new variable of integration. We observe that

$$(z - \cos \theta)^{n+m+1} = i^{n+m+1} \sin^{n+m+1} \theta \, e^{i(n+m+1)\psi},$$

$$z^2 - 1 = \cos^2 \theta + 2i \cos \theta \sin \theta \, e^{i\psi} - \sin^2 \theta \, e^{2i\psi} - 1$$

$$= e^{+i\psi} \left[(\cos^2 \theta - 1) e^{-i\psi} - \sin^2 \theta \, e^{i\psi} + 2i \cos \theta \sin \theta\right]$$

$$= 2i \sin \theta \, e^{i\psi} \left[\cos \theta + i \sin \theta \cos \psi\right],$$

and

$$dz = - \sin \theta \, e^{i\psi} \, d\psi.$$

If we now use these expressions in the integral we obtain immediately

$$P_n^m (\cos \theta) = \frac{i^m}{2\pi} \frac{(n + m)!}{m!} \int_{-\pi}^{\pi} [\cos \theta + i \sin \theta \cos \psi]^n \, e^{-im\psi} \, d\psi.$$

Another method of arriving at this type of integral is to work with the expression

$$V = [z + ix \cos u + iy \sin u]^n.$$

Since $V_{xx} = - \cos^2 u \, n(n - 1) [z + ix \cos u + iy \sin u]^{n-2}$

$$V_{yy} = - \sin^2 u \, n(n - 1) [z + ix \cos u + iy \sin u]^{n-2}$$

$$V_{zz} = n(n - 1) [z + ix \cos u + iy \sin u]^{n-2}$$

we see that $\Delta V = 0$.

Since u is a parameter we see that

$$\int_{-\pi}^{\pi} [z + ix \cos u + iy \sin u]^n \, e^{imu} \, du$$

is also a solution of Laplace's equation.

If we now replace x, y, and z by polar coordinates and let $\phi - u = \psi$ we obtain

$$r^n e^{im\phi} \int_{-\pi}^{\pi} [\cos \theta + i \sin \theta \cos \psi]^n e^{-im\psi} d\psi;$$

and comparison with the typical solution $r^n e^{im\phi} P_n^m(\cos \theta)$ shows us that $P_n^m(\cos \theta)$ must be proportional to the integral in the above expression. But we are now faced with the evaluation of a constant of integration, which was unnecessary in the previous method.

This last method was exploited very fruitfully by E. T. Whittaker, who worked with the general solution of Laplace's equation

$$V = \int_0^{2\pi} f(z + ix \cos u + iy \sin u, u) \, du.$$

If we now return to our integral representation we can observe that the integrand can be written as the sum of an even and an odd term; but since the interval of integration is $(-\pi, \pi)$ the latter term vanishes so that

$$P_n^m(\cos \theta) = \frac{i^m}{2\pi} \frac{(n+m)!}{n!} \int_{-\pi}^{\pi} [\cos \theta + i \sin \theta \cos \psi]^n \cos m \psi \, d\psi.$$

If we refer back to the differential equation for $P_n^m(t)$ we see that n enters the equation in the combination $n(n+1)$, which remains unchanged if n is replaced by $-n-1$. But the solution $r^n e^{im\phi} P_n^m(\cos \theta)$ becomes $r^{-n-1} e^{im\phi} P_n^m(\cos \theta)$. If we make the same change in the expression

$$\frac{(n+m)!}{n!} = (n+m)(n+m-1) \cdots (n+1)$$

we obtain

$$(-n-1+m)(-n-1+m-1) \cdots (-n) = (-1)^m \frac{n!}{(n-m)!} \cdot$$

Thus the left side of the integral representation remains unchanged and we obtain another representation,

$$P_n^m(\cos \theta) = \frac{(-i)^m n!}{2\pi(n-m)!} \int_{-\pi}^{\pi} \frac{\cos m \psi}{[\cos \theta + i \sin \theta \cos \psi]^{n+1}} d\psi \cdot$$

Since m enters the differential equation as m^2 and replacing m by $-m$ in the solution $r^n e^{im\phi} P_n^m(\cos \theta)$ leads to $r^n e^{-im\phi} P_n^{-m}(\cos \theta)$, we see that

$$P_n^{-m}(\cos \theta) = (i)^{-m} \frac{(n-m)!}{2\pi n!} \int_{-\pi}^{\pi} [\cos \theta + i \sin \theta \cos \psi]^n \cos m \psi \, d\psi$$

$$= \frac{i^m n!}{2\pi(n+m)!} \int_{-\pi}^{\pi} \frac{\cos m \psi}{[\cos \theta + i \sin \theta \cos \psi]^{n+1}} d\psi \cdot$$

A comparison of these expressions now shows us that

$$P_n^{-m}(\cos \theta) = (-1)^m \frac{(n-m)!}{(n+m)!} P_n^m(\cos \theta) \cdot$$

These integral representations were derived under the assumption that n and m were integers. In some applications it is desirable to remove these restrictions and one can use these integrals to define $P_n^m(\cos \theta)$ for arbitrary n and m, but the integrals must then be considered as contour integrals in the complex plane and the contour must be properly selected.

5. Boundary Value Problems

The functions discussed in the previous sections are of great value in finding solutions of certain boundary value problems in spherical coordinate systems. Suppose we seek a solution of the equation

$$\Delta V = 0$$

defined in the sphere $r = a$ and such that on $r = a$, V is a prescribed function of θ and ϕ—say $f(\theta, \phi)$. We now seek a solution of the form

$$V = \sum_{n=0}^{\infty} r^n \sum_{m=-n}^{n} A_{n,m} \, e^{im\phi} \, P_n^m(\cos \theta)$$

where the $A_{n,m}$ must be so selected that V satisfies the boundary conditions on $r = a$, that is,

$$f(\theta, \phi) = \sum_{n=0}^{\infty} a^n \sum_{m=-n}^{n} A_{n,m} \, e^{im\phi} \, P_n^m(\cos \theta) \, .$$

To evaluate the coefficients $A_{n,m}$ we observe that the family of functions $e^{im\phi} P_n^m(\cos \theta)$ is orthogonal over the two-dimensional manifold $0 \leq \theta \leq \pi$ and $0 \leq \phi \leq 2\pi$ with weight function $\sin \theta$—that is, over the surface area of the sphere. We have immediately

$$\int_0^{2\pi} \int_0^{\pi} e^{im\phi} \, P_n^m(\cos \theta) \, e^{-ik\phi} \, P_l^{-k}(\cos \theta) \sin \theta \, d\theta \, d\phi = 0$$

$$\text{for } m \neq k$$

since the integral can be written as a product of two independent integrals,

$$\int_0^{2\pi} e^{im\phi} e^{-ik\phi} \, d\phi \int_0^{\pi} \sin \theta \, P_n^m(\cos \theta) \, P_l^{-k}(\cos \theta) \, d\theta$$

and the first integral certainly vanishes for $m \neq k$. For $m = k$ the integral reduces to

$$2\pi \int_0^{\pi} \sin \theta \, P_n^m(\cos \theta) \, P_l^{-m}(\cos \theta) \, d\theta.$$

We now replace $\cos \theta$ by the variable t and let

$$P_n^m(t) = \frac{(-1)^m (1 - t^2)^{m/2}}{2^n n!} \left(\frac{d}{dt} \right)^{n+m} (t^2 - 1)^n$$

$$P_l^{-m}(t) = \frac{(-1)^{-m} (1 - t^2)^{-m/2}}{2^l l!} \left(\frac{d}{dt} \right)^{l-m} (t^2 - 1)^l \, ,$$

and the integral reduces to

$$\frac{2\pi}{(2^n n!)\,(2^l l!)} \int_{-1}^{1} \left[\left(\frac{d}{dt}\right)^{n+m} (t^2 - 1)^n \right] \left[\left(\frac{d}{dt}\right)^{l-m} (t^2 - 1)^l \right] dt \,.$$

After an m-fold integration by parts, and observing that the integrated terms vanish at $t = \pm 1$, we arrive at

$$\frac{2\pi(-)^m}{(2^n n!)\,(2^l l!)} \int_{-1}^{1} \left[\left(\frac{d}{dt}\right)^{n} (t^2 - 1)^n \right] \left[\left(\frac{d}{dt}\right)^{l} (t^2 - 1)^l \right] dt \,,$$

which is nothing but

$$2\pi(-)^m \int_{-1}^{1} P_n(t)\, P_l(t)\, dt.$$

But in Chapter 1 we saw that this integral vanishes for $n \neq l$ and for $n = l$ we have $4\pi/(2n + 1)$. Thus

$$\int_0^{2\pi} \int_0^{\pi} e^{im\phi}\, P_n^m(\cos\theta)\, e^{-ik\phi}\, P_l^{-k}(\cos\theta) \sin\theta\, d\theta\, d\phi$$

$$= 0 \qquad\qquad m \neq k \text{ or } \quad n \neq l$$

$$= \frac{4\pi(-)^m}{2n + 1} \qquad m = k \text{ and } n = l \,.$$

Use of this orthogonality relationship allows us to evaluate the $A_{n,m}$ by multiplying both sides of the defining relationship by $e^{-ik\phi} P_l^{-k}(\cos\theta)$ and integrating over the surface of the sphere so that

$$A_{l,k} = \frac{2l + 1}{4\pi a^l} (-)^k \int_0^{2\pi} \int_0^{\pi} f(\theta, \phi) \sin\theta\, e^{-ik\phi} P_l^{-k}(\cos\theta)\, d\theta\, d\phi \,.$$

Thus we see that the solution to our problem can be written as

$$V(r, \theta, \phi) = \frac{1}{4\pi} \int_0^{2\pi} \int_0^{\pi} f(\alpha, \beta) \sin\alpha \sum_{n=0}^{\infty} (2n + 1) \left(\frac{r}{a}\right)^n$$

$$\times \sum_{m=-n}^{n} (-)^m\, e^{im\phi}\, P_n^m(\cos\theta)\, e^{-im\beta}\, P_n^{-m}(\cos\alpha)\, d\alpha\, d\beta \,,$$

where α and β are introduced as variables of integration and θ and ϕ are the angular coordinates of the point at which V is evaluated. Using the relationship between P_n^{-m} and P_n^{m} we simplify the above to

$$V(r, \theta, \phi) = \frac{1}{4\pi} \int_0^{2\pi} \int_0^{\pi} f(\alpha, \beta) \sin\alpha \sum_{n=0}^{n} \left(\frac{r}{a}\right)^n (2n + 1) \left\{ P_n(\cos\theta)\, P_n(\cos\alpha) \right.$$

$$\left. + 2 \sum_{m=1}^{n} \frac{(n - m)!}{(n + m)!}\, P_n^m(\cos\theta)\, P_n^m(\cos\alpha)\, \cos m(\phi - \beta) \right\} d\alpha\, d\beta.$$

6. The Addition Theorem for the Legendre Polynomials

The above can be used to derive an important theorem in the theory of Legendre functions—namely, the addition theorem for the Legendre polynomials. We now hold the point (r, θ, ϕ) fixed and introduce a new polar coordinate system $(r, \boldsymbol{\theta}, \boldsymbol{\phi})$ that has as its polar axis the ray defined by the point (r, θ, ϕ) and the origin. Thus the new axis is defined by $\boldsymbol{\theta} = 0$. The new variables of integration are also referred to the new axis, and since α is the angle between the rays through the origin and defined by (θ, ϕ) and (α, β), it follows that

$$\cos \boldsymbol{\alpha} = \cos \theta \cos \alpha + \sin \theta \sin \alpha \cos (\phi - \beta).$$

Furthermore,

$$P_n(\cos \boldsymbol{\theta}) = P_n(1) = 1$$

$$P_n^m(\cos \boldsymbol{\theta}) = P_n^m(1) = 0, \qquad m > 0,$$

so that, when the integration is referred to the new coordinate system,

$$V(r, \theta, \phi) = \frac{1}{4\pi} \int_0^{2\pi} \int_0^{\pi} f(\alpha, \beta) \sin \alpha \sum_{n=0}^{n} (2n + 1) \left(\frac{r}{a}\right)^n P_n(\cos \boldsymbol{\alpha}) \, d\alpha \, d\beta .$$

The value of V at the point in question is independent of the particular coordinate system in which the integration is performed. Hence the two different expressions must be identical. In general, we cannot conclude from the equality of two integrals that the integrands are also equal. But here we see that the integrands contain an arbitrary function $f(\alpha, \beta)$, so that the difference between the two integrals,—namely,

$$\int_0^{2\pi} \int_0^{\pi} f(\alpha, \beta) \sin \alpha \sum_{n=0}^{\infty} (2n + 1) \left(\frac{r}{a}\right)^n \left\{ P_n(\cos \boldsymbol{\alpha}) - P_n(\cos \theta) \, P_n(\cos \alpha) \right.$$

$$\left. - 2 \sum_{m=1}^{n} \frac{(n - m)!}{(n + m)!} P_n^m(\cos \theta) \, P_n^m(\cos \alpha) \cos m \, (\phi - \beta) \right\} \, d\alpha \, d\beta ,$$

can vanish for all integrable $f(\alpha, \beta)$ if and only if the factor of $f(\alpha, \beta)$ vanishes. This factor is a sum of linearly independent terms and can vanish only if every term vanishes identically. Thus we see that

$$P_n \big[\cos \theta \cos \alpha + \sin \theta \sin \alpha \cos (\phi - \beta)\big]$$

$$= P_n(\cos \theta) \, P_n(\cos \alpha) + 2 \sum_{m=1}^{n} \frac{(n - m)!}{(n + m)!} P_n^m (\cos \theta)$$

$$\times P_n^m(\cos \alpha) \cos m \, (\phi - \beta).$$

This is the statement of the addition theorem for the Legendre polynomials.

The existence of such a theorem should not come as a complete surprise. Its existence can be inferred from physical principles. Evidently the equations of the form

$$\Delta V + k^2 V = 0,$$

$$\Delta V = \frac{1}{c^2} V_{tt},$$

$$\alpha^2 \Delta V = V_t$$

are invariant under rotations and translations of the coordinate system. This can be verified by direct computations, but it is obvious physically since these equations refer to physical processes, which are independent of the coordinate system to which we refer them. Thus any rigid transformation of the coordinate system should leave the equations invariant. We have seen that the equation

$$\Delta V = 0$$

has an infinite set of fundamental solutions of the form

$$r^n P_n^m(\cos \theta) \, e^{im\phi}, \quad r^{-n-1} P_n^m(\cos \theta) \, e^{im\phi}, \quad \text{where}$$

$$n = 0, 1, 2, \cdots, \quad m = 0, \pm 1, \pm 2, \cdots.$$

Hence if we choose any solution—say $r^n P_n(\cos \theta)$—and refer it to a new coordinate system, rotated relative to the original coordinate system, then it must be possible to express that solution in terms of the fundamental solutions in the new coordinate system. Thus it must be possible to find an expression of the form

$$r^n P_n[\cos \theta \cos \alpha + \sin \theta \sin \alpha \cos (\phi - \beta)]$$

$$= \sum_{m=-n}^{n} r^n c_m P_n^m(\cos \theta) \, e^{im\phi}$$

where the c_m must be found. This we did in the previous paragraphs. From this discussion it appears evident that it should be possible to find a similar theorem for solutions of the form $r^n P_n^m(\cos \theta) \, e^{im\phi}$, but this is a more complicated solution and we therefore expect the addition theorem to be correspondingly more complex. Such a theorem has been found, but is beyond the scope of this book. Similarly, addition theorems for translations of the coordinate system have been found. Such theorems have been found for many classes of solutions of these equations in different coordinate systems. In the next chapter, we shall discover some other addition theorems in cylindrical coordinates.

7. Recurrence Formulas

We saw in Chapter 1 that the orthogonal functions satisfy recurrence relationships. We will now derive some recurrence formulas for the associated

Legendre functions. The recurrence formula for the Legendre polynomials derived in Chapter 1 is

$$(n + 1) P_{n+1}(t) - (2n + 1)t P_n(t) + n P_{n-1}(t) = 0.$$

We differentiate the equation m times and multiply by $(-)^m(1 - t^2)^{m/2}$. We then obtain, using the fact that

$$(-)^m(1 - t^2)^{m/2} \left(\frac{d}{dt}\right)^m P_n(t) = P_n^m(t),$$

$$(n + 1) P_{n+1}^m(t) - (2n + 1)t P_n^m(t) + n P_{n-1}^m(t)$$
$$+ m(2n + 1) \sqrt{1 - t^2} P_n^{m-1}(t) = 0 .$$

In the above formula there are variations in both superscripts and subscripts. We can derive a related formula, however, where the superscripts are fixed. To do so we first observe that the recurrence formula for the Legendre polynomials tells us that

$$P_n(1) = 1, \qquad P_n(-1) = (-1)^n,$$

because these values satisfy the equation at $t = \pm 1$ respectively. Next we see that

$$\frac{d}{dt} \left[P_{n+1}(t) - P_{n-1}(t)\right] = \sum_{k=0}^{n} a_k P_k(t) ,$$

because the left side is a polynomial of degree n. Thus, from the orthogonality of the Legendre polynomials we have

$$a_k = \frac{2k + 1}{2} \int_{-1}^{1} P_k(t) \frac{d}{dt} \left[P_{n+1}(t) - P_{n-1}(t)\right] dt .$$

After an integration by parts we have

$$a_k = -\frac{2k + 1}{2} \int_{-1}^{1} \left[P_{n+1}(t) - P_{n-1}(t)\right] P_k'(t) dt ,$$

where the integrated terms vanish by virtue of the derived values of $P_n(\pm 1)$. $P_k'(t)$ is of degree $k - 1$. Therefore for $k = 0, 1, \cdots, n - 1$, $a_k = 0$ because $P_{n+1}(t)$ and $P_{n-1}(t)$ are orthogonal to all polynomials of degree $n - 2$ or lower. To obtain a_n we have

$$a_n = -\frac{2n + 1}{2} \int_{-1}^{1} \left[P_{n+1}(t) - P_{n-1}(t)\right] P_n'(t) dt = \frac{2n + 1}{2} \int_{-1}^{1} P_{n-1}(t) P_n'(t) dt,$$

since $P_{n+1}(t)$ is orthogonal to $P_n'(t)$. Integration by parts now yields

$$a_n = \frac{2n + 1}{2} \left\{ \left[P_{n-1}(t) P_n(t)\right]_{-1}^{1} - \int_{-1}^{1} P_n(t) P_{n-1}'(t) dt \right\} = 2n + 1 .$$

Thus

$$\frac{d}{dt}\left[P_{n+1}(t) - P_{n-1}(t)\right] = (2n + 1)\, P_n(t)\,.$$

We now differentiate $(m - 1)$ times and multiply by $(-1)^m(1 - t^2)^{m/2}$ to obtain

$$P_{n+1}^m(t) - P_{n-1}^m(t) = -(2n + 1)\sqrt{1 - t^2}\, P_n^{m-1}(t)\,.$$

We can now eliminate $P_n^{m-1}(t)$ from the previously derived recurrence formula and obtain

$$(n + 1 - m)\, P_{n+1}^m(t) - (2n + 1)t\, P_n^m(t) + (n + m)\, P_{n-1}^m(t) = 0.$$

A recurrence formula in which the subscripts are fixed can be derived from the differential equation

$$(1 - t^2)\left(\frac{d}{dt}\right)^2 P_n(t) - 2t\left(\frac{d}{dt}\right) P_n(t) + n(n + 1)\, P_n(t) = 0\,.$$

We differentiate the equation m times and multiply by $(-)^m(1 - t^2)^{m/2}$ and obtain immediately

$$P_n^{m+2}(t) + \frac{2(m+1)t}{\sqrt{1 - t^2}}\, P_n^{m+1}(t) + (n - m)\,(n + m + 1)\, P_n^m(t) = 0\,.$$

8. Asymptotic Formulas

In many applications it is important to know how the Legendre functions behave for large values of the parameter n. We saw in Chapter 1 that it is possible to expand functions in series of Legendre polynomials. To establish the convergence of the series it is necessary to know these asymptotic formulas. Some of this information we can derive directly from the differential equation. If in

$$P_n''(\cos\theta) + \cot\theta\, P_n'(\cos\theta) + n(n + 1)\, P_n(\cos\theta) = 0$$

we let

$$P_n(\cos\theta) = \frac{u(\theta)}{\sqrt{\sin\theta}}$$

we obtain

$$u''(\theta) + \left[\left(n + \frac{1}{2}\right)^2 + \frac{1}{4\sin^2\theta}\right] u = 0\,.$$

For large values of n we can neglect the term $1/(4\sin^2\theta)$, except for values of θ close to zeros of $\sin\theta$. This simplified equation is harmonic, so that we can write

$$P_n(\cos\theta) \approx \frac{A_n\cos\left[\left(n + \frac{1}{2}\right)\theta + \phi_n\right]}{\sqrt{\sin\theta}}\,.$$

In this asymptotic formula we have an unknown amplitude and phase, which may depend on n. To evaluate A_n we recall that

$$\int_0^\pi \sin\theta\, P_n^2(\cos\theta)\, d\theta = \frac{2}{2n+1}.$$

If we replace $P_n(\cos\theta)$ by its asymptotic form and integrate, we find that

$$A_n \approx \sqrt{\frac{2}{\pi n}}.$$

Strictly speaking, we should not use the asymptotic formula near $\theta = 0$, and π. But since $P_n(t)$ is a polynomial it is bounded near $t = \pm 1$, which is equivalent to $\theta = 0$ or π. Then one can show that the error introduced can be made smaller than any preassigned ϵ by working with a sufficiently large n.

To determine ϕ_n we examine the generating function for $\theta = \pi/2$;

$$\frac{1}{\sqrt{1+r^2}} = \sum_{n=0}^\infty P_n(0)\, r^n.$$

We see from the binomial expansion of the left side that for odd values of n, $P_n(0)$ vanishes and for even values of n we have an alternation in sign. From this consideration it follows that $\phi_n = -\pi/4$. Thus we find

$$P_n(\cos\theta) \approx \sqrt{\frac{2}{\pi n \sin\theta}} \cos\left[\left(n+\frac{1}{2}\right)\theta - \frac{\pi}{4}\right],$$

for large values of n, and $0 < \epsilon \le \theta \le \pi - \epsilon < \pi$. Similarly we can show that

$$n^{-m} P_n^m(\cos\theta) \approx \sqrt{\frac{2}{\pi n \sin\theta}} \cos\left[\left(n+\frac{1}{2}\right)\theta - \frac{\pi}{4} + \frac{m\pi}{2}\right]$$

for $n \gg m$, $0 < \epsilon \le \theta \le \pi - \epsilon$.

Exercises

1. Show that

$$P_n'(t) = (2n-1)\, P_{n-1}(t) + (2n-5)\, P_{n-3}(t) + \cdots.$$

2. Use Leibniz' rule and Rodriques' formula for the Legendre polynomial to show that

$$(1-t)^n\, P_n\left(\frac{1+t}{1-t}\right) = \sum_{k=0}^n \binom{n}{k}^2 t^k.$$

3. Use the generating function of the Legendre polynomials to show that

$$P_n(\cos\theta) = \frac{(2n)!}{2^{2n}n!^2}\left[\cos n\theta + \frac{1}{1}\frac{n}{2n-1}\cos(n-2)\theta\right.$$

$$+ \frac{1\times 3}{1\times 2}\frac{n(n-1)}{(2n-1)(2n-3)}\cos(n-4)\theta + \frac{1\times 3\times 5}{1\times 2\times 3}$$

$$\times\frac{n(n-1)(n-2)}{(2n-1)(2n-3)(2n-5)}\cos(n-6)\theta + \cdots\left.\right].$$

4. Use the previous exercise to show that

$$|P_n(t)| \leq 1 \quad \text{for} \quad |t| \leq |1.$$

5. Show that

$$P_n(t) = \frac{(2n)!}{2^n(n!)^2}t^n{}_2F_1\left(-\frac{n}{2},\frac{1-n}{2};\frac{1}{2}-n;\frac{1}{t^2}\right).$$

(See Section 14 of Chapter 1.)

6. Show that

$$t^k = \frac{k!}{3\times 5\cdots(2k+1)}\left\{(2k+1)P_k(t) + (2k-3)\frac{2k+1}{2}P_{k-2}(t)\right.$$

$$+ (2k-7)\frac{(2k+1)(2k-1)}{2\times 4}P_{k-4}(t) + \cdots\left.\right\}.$$

7. Show that if

$$f(x) = \sum_{n=0}^{\infty}A_n P_n(x),$$

$$\int_1^x f(x)\,dx = -A_0 - \frac{1}{3}A_1 + \sum_{n=1}^{\infty}\left(\frac{A_{n-1}}{2n-1} - \frac{A_{n+1}}{2n+3}\right)P_n(x).$$

Hence show that

$$\sin^{-1}x = \frac{\pi}{2}\sum_{n=0}^{\infty}\left\{\frac{1\times 3\cdots(2n-1)}{2\times 4\cdots 2n}\right\}^2\left[P_{2n+1}(x) - P_{2n-1}(x)\right].$$

8. Show that the differential equation

$$(1-t^2)y'' - 2ty' + \lambda y = 0$$

has polynomial solutions only if $\lambda = n(n+1)$, where n is an integer.

(Assume a solution of the form $y = \sum_0^{\infty}A_k x^k$.)

9. Show that the associated Legendre equation is satisfied by the equivalent expressions

$$\left(\frac{t+1}{t-1}\right)^{m/2} \left(\frac{d}{dt}\right)^n \left[(x+1)^{n-m} (x-1)^{n+m}\right]$$

$$= \left(\frac{t-1}{t+1}\right)^{m/2} \left(\frac{d}{dt}\right)^n \left[(x+1)^{n+m} (x-1)^{n-m}\right].$$

10. Show that the function $Q_n(t) = \dfrac{1}{2n+1} \displaystyle\int_{-1}^{1} \dfrac{(1-z^2)^n}{(t-z)^{n+1}} \, dz$,

which is known as the Legendre function of the second kind, satisfies Legendre's differential equation.

[3]

Bessel Functions

1. Introduction

In Chapter 2 we saw that attempts to solve Laplace's equation in spherical coordinates led to Legendre's differential equation. We now turn to the two-dimensional wave equation in cylindrical coordinates:

$$c^2\left[u_{\rho\rho} + \frac{1}{\rho} u_\rho + \frac{1}{\rho^2} u_{\phi\phi}\right] = u_{tt}.$$

Applying the method of separation of variables, we let

$$u = R(\rho)\, E(\phi)\, e^{iwt},$$

where we assume that the time dependence is harmonic. If we insert this in the differential equation, divide by u, and let $w^2/c^2 = k^2$ we obtain

$$\rho^2 \frac{R''(\rho)}{R(\rho)} + \rho \frac{R'(\rho)}{R(\rho)} + \frac{E''(\phi)}{E(\phi)} + \rho^2 k^2 = 0.$$

From this we can conclude that

$$\frac{E''(\phi)}{E(\phi)} = -m^2$$

$$\rho^2 \frac{R''(\rho)}{R(\rho)} + \rho \frac{R'(\rho)}{R(\rho)} - m^2 + \rho^2 k^2 = 0.$$

The first of these has the solutions

$$E = c_1\, e^{im\phi} + c_2\, e^{-im\phi}.$$

The second equation is Bessel's equation and is usually written in the form

$$R''(\rho) + \frac{1}{\rho} R'(\rho) + \left(k^2 - \frac{m^2}{\rho^2}\right) R(\rho) = 0.$$

If we let $\rho = x/k$ and let $R(\rho) = y(x)$ it has the form

$$y''(x) + \frac{1}{x} y'(x) + \left(1 - \frac{m^2}{x^2}\right) y(x) = 0;$$

a solution of this equation is usually denoted by the symbol $J_m(x)$. Like Legendre functions the Bessel functions cannot be expressed in terms of elementary

42

functions. But we will show that we can treat these functions as limiting cases of the Legendre functions. That this is so can be inferred not only from mathematical reasoning but also from physical reasoning. We construct a tangent plane to the sphere $r = a$ at the north pole—that is, at the point $x = y = 0$. In spherical coordinates we can write

$$x = r \sin \theta \cos \phi$$

$$y = r \sin \theta \sin \phi$$

$$z = r \cos \theta,$$

but for small values of θ, on the sphere, we can write

$$x = a\theta \cos \phi$$

$$y = a\theta \sin \phi$$

$$z = a$$

and we see that this is a polar coordinate system on the plane $z = a$, where the radial distance is $a\theta$. Thus we expect that for small values of θ, P_n^m and J_m should be closely related. We can show directly that if we start with Legendre's differential equation

$$\frac{1}{\sin \theta} \frac{d}{d\theta} \sin \theta \frac{dy}{d\theta} + \left[n(n + 1) - \frac{m^2}{\sin^2 \theta} \right] y = 0,$$

let $\theta = x/n$, and go to the limit, as $n \to \infty$ we obtain Bessel's equation. We see that for small values of θ we can write the equation in the form

$$\frac{1}{\theta} \frac{d}{d\theta} \theta \frac{dy}{d\theta} + \left[n(n + 1) - \frac{m^2}{\theta^2} \right] y = 0,$$

and making the substitution $\theta = x/n$ we obtain

$$\frac{1}{x} \frac{d}{dx} x \frac{dy}{dx} + \left[n \frac{(n + 1)}{n^2} - \frac{m^2}{x^2} \right] y = 0.$$

If we now let $n \to \infty$ and expand the first term we have Bessel's equation

$$y'' + \frac{1}{x} y' + \left[1 - \frac{m^2}{x^2} \right] y = 0.$$

2. Integral Representations

We can derive integral representations for the Bessel functions by suitable limiting processes in the integral representations for the Legendre functions. We saw in Chapter 2 that

$$P_n^m(\cos \theta) = \frac{i^m}{2\pi} \frac{(n + m)!}{n!} \int_{-\pi}^{\pi} [\cos \theta + i \sin \theta \cos \psi]^n e^{-im\psi} \, d\psi .$$

We would like to replace θ by x/n and let $n \to \infty$, but because the factor of the integral depends on n and tends to infinity, we divide both sides by that factor and obtain

$$\frac{n!}{(n+m)!} \, P_n^m\left(\cos \frac{x}{n}\right) = \frac{i^m}{2\pi} \int_{-\pi}^{\pi} \left[\cos \frac{x}{n} + i \sin \frac{x}{n} \cos \psi\right]^n e^{-im\psi} \, d\psi \, .$$

To take the limit as $n \to \infty$ we observe that when x/n is small

$$\left[\cos \frac{x}{n} + i \sin \frac{x}{n} \cos \psi\right]^n \approx \left[1 + i \, \frac{x}{n} \cos \psi\right]^n ,$$

and from the definition of e it follows that

$$\lim_{n-\infty} \left[1 + i \, \frac{x}{n} \cos \psi\right]^n = e^{ix \cos \psi} \, .$$

We thus obtain

$$\lim_{n\to\infty} \frac{n!}{(n+m)!} \, P_n^m\left(\cos \frac{x}{n}\right) = \frac{i^m}{2\pi} \int_{-\pi}^{\pi} e^{i[x\cos\psi-m\psi]} \, d\psi \, .$$

The latter integral must be a solution of Bessel's equation; it is usually written

$$J_m(x) = \frac{i^{-m}}{2\pi} \int_{-\pi}^{\pi} e^{i[x\cos\psi-m\psi]} \, d\psi \, .$$

We see therefore that

$$\lim_{n\to\infty} \frac{n! \, P_n^m\left(\cos \dfrac{x}{n}\right)}{(n+m)!} = (-)^m \, J_m(x) \, .$$

Furthermore, we see from the integral that $J_{-m}(x) = (-1)^m \, J_m(x)$.

Another result, which we can obtain as an immediate consequence of these limiting processes, is to return to

$$P_n^m(t) = (-)^m \, (1 - t^2)^{m/2} \left(\frac{d}{dt}\right)^m P_n(t)$$

and let $t = \cos x/n$. Then

$$1 - t^2 = \sin^2 \frac{x}{n} \approx \left(\frac{x}{n}\right)^2$$

$$\frac{du}{dt} = \frac{\dfrac{du}{dx}}{\dfrac{dt}{dx}} = \frac{-1}{\dfrac{1}{n} \cdot \sin \dfrac{x}{n}} \frac{du}{dx} \approx - \frac{n^2}{x} \frac{du}{dx} \, .$$

Furthermore, we recognize the fact that

$$\lim_{n\to\infty} \frac{n! \, n^m}{(n+m)!} = \lim_{n\to\infty} \frac{n^m}{(n+m)(n+m-1)\cdots(n+1)} = 1 \, .$$

Now we can write

$$\frac{n! \, P_n^m\left(\cos \frac{x}{n}\right)}{(n+m)!} \approx (-)^m \left(\frac{x}{n}\right)^m \frac{(-n^2)^m n!}{(n+m)!} \left(\frac{d}{xdx}\right)^m P_n\left(\cos \frac{x}{n}\right)$$

and in the limit as $n \to \infty$ we obtain

$$(-)^m J_m(x) = x^m \left(\frac{d}{xdx}\right)^m J_0(x) \, .$$

Thus we see that we can generate all Bessel functions, of integral order, by performing the indicated m-fold operation on $J_0(x)$. Another consequence of this statement is the following:

$$(-)^{m+1} J_{m+1}(x) = x^{m+1} \left(\frac{d}{xdx}\right)^{m+1} J_0(x) = x^{m+1} \frac{d}{xdx} x^{-m} \left[x^m \left(\frac{d}{xdx}\right)^m J_0(x)\right]$$

$$= x^{m+1} \frac{d}{xdx} (-)^m x^{-m} J_m(x) \, .$$

The latter can be put into the form

$$\frac{d}{xdx} \frac{J_m(x)}{x^m} = - \frac{J_{m+1}(x)}{x^{m+1}} \, .$$

By combining the last statement and the previously derived integral representation we can derive another integral representation known as Poisson's integral representation.
We write

$$J_0(x) = \frac{1}{2\pi} \int_{-\pi}^{\pi} e^{ix \cos \psi} \, d\psi = \frac{2}{\pi} \int_0^{\pi/2} \cos [x \cos \psi] \, d\psi$$

and now obtain

$$J_1(x) = - \frac{d}{dx} J_0(x) = - \frac{d}{dx} \frac{2}{\pi} \int_0^{\pi/2} \cos [x \cos \psi] \, d\psi \, .$$

We now differentiate under the integral sign and perform an integration by parts:

$$J_1(x) = \frac{2}{\pi} \left[\sin \psi \sin [x \cos \psi]_0^{\pi/2} + x \int_0^{\pi/2} \sin^2 \psi \cos [x \cos \psi] \, d\psi\right]$$

$$= \frac{2x}{\pi} \int_0^{\pi/2} \sin^2 \psi \cos [x \cos \psi] \, d\psi \, .$$

Similarly, from

$$J_2(x) = - x^2 \frac{d}{xdx} \frac{J_1(x)}{x}$$

we find

$$J_2(x) = \frac{2}{\pi} \frac{x^2}{3} \int_0^{\pi/2} \sin^4 \psi \, \cos \, [x \cos \psi] \, d\psi$$

and in general

$$J_m(x) = \frac{2}{\pi} \frac{x^m}{1 \times 3 \times \cdots \times (2m-1)} \int_0^{\pi/2} \sin^{2m} \psi \, \cos \, [x \cos \psi] \, d\psi \, .$$

If we return to

$$\frac{d}{dx} \frac{J_m(x)}{x^m} = - \frac{J_{m+1}(x)}{x^{m+1}}$$

and replace m by $-m$ we see that

$$\frac{d}{dx} x^m \, J_{-m}(x) = - x^{m-1} \, J_{1-m}(x) \, ,$$

and since $J_{-m}(x) = (-1)^m \, J_m(x)$, we obtain

$$\frac{d}{dx} x^m \, J_m(x) = x^m \, J_{m-1}(x) \, .$$

From this we see that

$$\frac{d}{dx} x \, J_1(x) = x \, J_0(x)$$

or

$$x \, J_1(x) = \int_0^x t \, J_0(t) \, dt$$

Similarly, by letting $m = 2$ we find

$$x^2 \, J_2(x) = \int_0^x t^2 \, J_1(t) \, dt = \int_0^x t \int_0^t \tau \, J_0(\tau) \, d\tau \, dt \, .$$

By interchanging the order of integration in the last integral we find that

$$x^2 \, J_2(x) = \frac{1}{2} \int_0^x t(x^2 - t^2) \, J_0(t) \, dt \, .$$

A repetition of this process shows that

$$x^3 \, J_3(x) = \int_0^x t^3 \, J_2(t) \, dt = \int_0^x t \, \frac{1}{2} \int_0^t \tau(t^2 - \tau^2) \, J_0(\tau) \, d\tau \, dt$$

$$= \frac{1}{2^3} \int_0^x t(x^2 - t^2)^2 \, J_0(t) \, dt \, .$$

Ultimately we obtain, as can readily be verified by induction,

$$x^{m+1} J_{m+1}(x) = \frac{1}{2^m m!} \int_0^x t(x^2 - t^2)^m J_0(t) \, dt \, .$$

Furthermore, by letting $t = x \sin \theta$, we can make the limits independent of x, so that

$$J_{m+1}(x) = \frac{x^{m+1}}{2^m m!} \int_0^{\pi/2} \sin \theta \cos^{2m+1} \theta \, J_0(x \sin \theta) \, d\theta \, .$$

Thus we see that we can obtain $J_m(x)$ from $J_0(x)$ by differentiation as well as by integration processes.

3. Recurrence Formula; Generating Function; Series Representation

The Bessel functions satisfy a recurrence formula as do the Legendre functions. We can derive it by returning to

$$P_n^{m+2}(t) + \frac{2(m + 1)t}{\sqrt{1 - t^2}} P_n^{m+1}(t) + (n - m)(n + m + 1) P_n^m(t) = 0 \, .$$

If we now again let $t = \cos x/n$, divide the equation by n^{m+2}, and let $n \to \infty$ we obtain

$$J_{m+2}(x) - \frac{2(m + 1)}{x} J_{m+1}(x) + J_m(x) = 0 \, .$$

The representation

$$J_m(x) = \frac{i^{-m}}{2\pi} \int_{-\pi}^{\pi} e^{i[x \cos \psi - m\psi]} \, d\psi$$

becomes, after letting $\psi = v - \pi/2$,

$$J_m(x) = \frac{1}{2\pi} \int_{-\pi}^{\pi} e^{ix \sin v} e^{-imv} \, dv \, .$$

The last integral can be interpreted as a Fourier coefficient of the periodic function $e^{ix \sin v}$. In other words, we can write

$$e^{ix \sin v} = \sum_{m=-\infty}^{\infty} J_m(x) \, e^{imv} \, .$$

By letting $e^{iv} = t$ we obtain the generating function of the Bessel functions,— namely,

$$e^{x(t-1/t)/2} = \sum_{m=-\infty}^{\infty} J_m(x) \, t^m \, .$$

It is interesting to observe that some books use this relationship as the starting point for a study of Bessel functions. We will now derive from it a power series for $J_m(x)$.

$$e^{x(t-1/t)/2} = e^{xt/2} \, e^{-x/2t} = \left(\sum_{n=0}^{\infty} \frac{x^n t^n}{2^n n!} \right) \left(\sum_{k=0}^{\infty} \frac{(-x)^k}{2^k t^k k!} \right)$$

$$= \sum_{m=0}^{\infty} t^m \left(\frac{x}{2} \right)^m \sum_{k=0}^{\infty} \frac{\left(-\dfrac{x}{2} \right)^{2k}}{k! \, (k+m)!}$$

$$+ \sum_{m=1}^{\infty} t^{-m} \left(-\frac{x}{2} \right)^m \sum_{k=0}^{\infty} \frac{\left(-\dfrac{x}{2} \right)^{2k}}{k! \, (k+m)!}.$$

Thus we see that

$$J_m(x) = \left(\frac{x}{2} \right)^m \sum_{k=0}^{\infty} \frac{\left(-\dfrac{x}{2} \right)^{2k}}{k! \, (k+m)!}, \qquad m \geq 0.$$

4. Addition Theorem

In Chapter 2 we derived an addition theorem for the Legendre polynomials —namely,

$$P_n(\cos \gamma) = P_n(\cos \theta) \, P_n(\cos \alpha) + 2 \sum_{m=1}^{n} \frac{(n-m)!}{(n+m)!} P_n^m(\cos \theta)$$

$$\times P_n^m(\cos \alpha) \cos m(\phi - \beta),$$

where $\cos \gamma = \cos \theta \cos \alpha + \sin \theta \sin \alpha \cos (\phi - \beta)$.

We now let $\theta = r/n$ and $\alpha = \rho/n$ and let n approach infinity in the addition theorem, and see that

$$\lim_{n \to \infty} \frac{n^{2m}(n-m)!}{(n+m)!} = \lim_{n \to \infty} \frac{n^{2m}}{(n+m)(n+m-1) \cdots (n-m+1)} = 1.$$

Furthermore,

$$\cos \gamma = \cos \frac{r}{n} \cos \frac{\rho}{n} + \sin \frac{r}{n} \sin \frac{\rho}{n} \cos (\phi - \beta)$$

$$\approx 1 - \frac{1}{2n^2} [r^2 + \rho^2 - 2r\rho \cos (\phi - \beta)]$$

so that $\lim_{n \to \infty} P_n(\cos \gamma) = J_0(R)$, where $R = \sqrt{r^2 + \rho^2 - 2r\rho \cos (\phi - \beta)}$.

Thus we find that

$$J_0(R) = J_0(r) \, J_0(\rho) + 2 \sum_{m=0}^{\infty} J_m(r) \, J_m(\rho) \cos^m (\phi - \beta).$$

The physical interpretation of this addition theorem is the following. In the case of the Legendre polynomials the addition theorem resulted from a choice of a new z axis that made some angle with the old axis. This can be interpreted as a rotation of the coordinate system about the origin. We saw that in deriving the Bessel functions from the Legendre functions we considered a polar coordinate system in a tangent plane at the north pole of the coordinate sphere. The rotation of the coordinate system for small angles is equivalent to a translation of the origin in the tangent plane. From the following diagram we see that

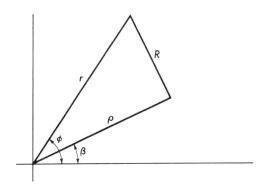

if we consider a point with polar coordinates r, ϕ and choose a new origin at the point ρ, β, the new polar distance is R, by the law of cosines.

5. Asymptotic Approximations and Zeros of Bessel Functions

In Chapter 2 we saw that for large values of n it was possible to approximate Legendre functions by simple trigonometric terms. In particular we derived the approximation

$$n^{-m} P_n^m(\cos \theta) \approx \sqrt{\frac{2}{\pi n \sin \theta}} \cos \left[\left(n + \frac{1}{2}\right)\theta + \frac{m\pi}{2} - \frac{\pi}{4}\right].$$

If we now let $\theta = x/n$ and let n become infinite the left side becomes a Bessel function and we obtain

$$(-)^m J_m(x) \approx \sqrt{\frac{2}{\pi x}} \cos \left[x + \frac{m\pi}{2} - \frac{\pi}{4}\right]$$

or

$$J_m(x) \approx \sqrt{\frac{2}{\pi x}} \cos \left[x - \frac{m\pi}{2} - \frac{\pi}{4}\right].$$

Since we expect the asymptotic form to be more accurate for large n we might be tempted to expect the above formula to be exact for Bessel functions. But as n approaches infinity $\theta = x/n$ approaches zero, at which point the asymptotic formula breaks down. Thus we expect that the formula for the Bessel functions can hold only for values of x, which are large. Thus we have arrived at an asymptotic formula for the Bessel functions as x approaches infinity.

We see from this asymptotic form that the Bessel functions have an infinity of zeros and the large ones can be evaluated by means of the asymptotic formula. Thus we see that

$$J_0(x) = 0$$

has the approximate zeros

$$x_k \approx (2k - 1)\frac{\pi}{2} + \frac{\pi}{4}.$$

The following table shows the degree of accuracy furnished by this approximation.

k	x_k approximate	x_k exact	percent error
1	2.355	2.405	2.10
2	5.496	5.520	.43
3	8.638	8.654	.18
4	11.779	11.792	.11
5	14.921	14.931	.07

Furthermore, almost all zeros are simple. This follows from the asymptotic formula for large zeros. That this is true in general follows from the following considerations. At a multiple zero not only $J_m(x)$ but also its derivative would vanish. If this point were a regular point of the second-order differential equation then zero initial value and zero initial derivative would imply that the solution vanished identically. Hence we have multiple zeros at worst only at singular points. Now the equation

$$J_m''(x) + \frac{1}{x} J_m'(x) + \left(1 - \frac{m^2}{x^2}\right) J_m(x) = 0$$

has a singularity at $x = 0$. Thus the only possible multiple zero of $J_m(x)$ is at $x = 0$. From the infinite series expression we see that $J_m(x)$ has an m-tuple zero at $x = 0$. But all other zeros must be simple.

6. Orthogonality Properties

In Chapter 1 we discussed orthogonal polynomials. These are special cases of orthogonal functions in general. We will show that the family of functions

$$\{J_0(\lambda_i x)\}, \qquad i = 1, 2, \cdots,$$

where $J_0(\lambda_i) = 0$, is orthogonal over the interval $(0, 1)$ with weight function x.

To prove this we write the differential equation for two members of this family —namely, $J_0(\lambda_i x)$ and $J_0(\lambda_k x)$ in the form

$$\frac{d}{dx} x \frac{d}{dx} J_0(\lambda_i x) + \lambda_i^2 x \, J_0(\lambda_i x) = 0$$

$$\frac{d}{dx} x \frac{d}{dx} J_0(\lambda_k x) + \lambda_k^2 x \, J_0(\lambda_k x) = 0 \,.$$

We now multiply the first of these equations by $J_0(\lambda_k x)$, the second by $J_0(\lambda_i x)$ and subtract the second from the first, and integrate over the interval $(0, 1)$:

$$\int_0^1 \left[J_0(\lambda_k x) \frac{d}{dx} x \frac{d}{dx} J_0(\lambda_i x) - J_0(\lambda_i x) \frac{d}{dx} x \frac{d}{dx} J_0(\lambda_k x) \right] dx$$

$$+ (\lambda_i^2 - \lambda_k^2) \int_0^1 x \, J_0(\lambda_k x) \, J_0(\lambda_i x) \, dx = 0 \,.$$

After an integration by parts we find

$$\int_0^1 x \, J_0(\lambda_k x) \, J_0(\lambda_i x) \, dx = \frac{J_0(\lambda_i x) \, x \frac{d}{dx} J_0(\lambda_k x) - J_0(\lambda_k x) \, x \frac{d}{dx} J_0(\lambda_k x) \,|_{x=1}}{\lambda_i^2 - \lambda_k^2} \,.$$

So far we have not used the particular properties of the numbers λ_i and λ_k. When $J_0(\lambda_i) = J_0(\lambda_k) = 0$ we observe that the numerator of the above expression vanishes. Thus we have

$$\int_0^1 x \, J_0(\lambda_k x) \, J_0(\lambda_i x) \, dx = 0 \,, \qquad i \neq k \,.$$

When $i = k$ or equivalently $\lambda_i = \lambda_k$ the denominator also vanishes and the expression on the right becomes indeterminate. To evaluate it we let $J_0(\lambda_k) = 0$, but let λ_i approach λ_k as a limit. Then we can use L'Hospital's rule to evaluate the right side:

$$\lim_{\lambda_i \to \lambda_k} \frac{J_0(\lambda_i) \, x \frac{d}{dx} J_0(\lambda_k x) \,|_{x=1}}{\lambda_i^2 - \lambda_k^2} = \lim_{\lambda_i \to \lambda_k} \frac{- J_0(\lambda_i) \lambda_k J_1(\lambda_k)}{\lambda_i^2 - \lambda_k^2}$$

$$= \lim_{\lambda_i \to \lambda_k} \frac{- \frac{d}{d\lambda_i} J_0(\lambda_i) \lambda_k J_1(\lambda_k)}{2\lambda_i} = \frac{1}{2} \, J_1^2(\lambda_k) \,.$$

Thus we have

$$\int_0^1 x \, J_0^2(\lambda_k x) \, dx = \frac{1}{2} \, J_1^2(\lambda_k) \,.$$

In Chapter 1 we saw that the sets of orthogonal polynomials treated were complete. In other words, it was possible to represent certain functions as infinite sums of such polynomials. The proof furnished there applied to orthogonal polynomials only, but many other families of orthogonal functions are also complete. The set of functions $\{J_0(\lambda_i x)\}$, where $J_0(\lambda_i) = 0$, is also a complete orthogonal set. Given an integrable function $f(x)$ defined over the interval $(0, 1)$, we can represent it in the form

$$f(x) = \sum_{k=1}^{\infty} a_k J_0(\lambda_k x) ,$$

where

$$a_k = \frac{\int_0^1 xf(x) J_0(\lambda_k x)\, dx}{\int_0^1 x\, J_0^2(\lambda_k x)\, dx} = \frac{\int_0^1 xf(x) J_0(\lambda_k x)\, dx}{\frac{1}{2}\, J_1^2(\lambda_k)} .$$

Expansions of this type are known as Fourier-Bessel series.

7. Applications to Boundary Value Problems

We will now consider an application of Bessel functions to a typical boundary value problem. We consider heat flow in a circular plate of radius 1. The boundary will be kept at zero temperature, and at time $t = 0$ we assume that the temperature is a function of r only. We now state the problem mathematically. We seek a solution of the equation

$$\Delta u = u_t$$

in polar coordinates, subject to the boundary condition

$$u(1, \theta, t) = 0$$

and the initial condition

$$u(r, \theta, 0) = f(r).$$

From the symmetry of the boundary and initial conditions we see that the solution will be independent of the angular coordinate θ. Thus the differential equation becomes

$$u_{rr} + \frac{1}{r}\, u_r = u_t .$$

In accordance with the method of separation of variables we write

$$u = R(r)\, T(t)$$

and find that

$$\frac{R''(r)}{R(r)} + \frac{1}{r}\, \frac{R'(r)}{R(r)} = \frac{T'(t)}{T(t)} = -\, \lambda^2 .$$

Then $T(t) = e^{-\lambda^2 t}$ and $R(r)$ satisfies Bessel's equation

$$R''(r) + \frac{1}{r} R'(r) + \lambda^2 R(r) = 0$$

so that $R(r) = J_0(\lambda r)$. To satisfy the boundary condition

$$u(1, t) = 0$$

we require that $J_0(\lambda) = 0$. We saw earlier that this equation has an infinity of zeros $\lambda_1, \lambda_2, \cdots$ and the set of functions $\{J_0(\lambda_i x)\}$ is a complete orthogonal set. Therefore the general solution of this equation must have the form

$$u = \sum_1^\infty a_k \, J_0(\lambda_k r) \, e^{-\lambda_k^2 \, t} \, .$$

To find a_k we use the initial condition

$$\sum_1^\infty a_k \, J_0(\lambda_k r) = f(r)$$

from which we see that

$$a_k = \frac{\displaystyle\int_0^1 r f(r) \, J_0(\lambda_k r) \, dr}{\frac{1}{2} \, J_1^2(\lambda_k)} \, .$$

The final solution to our problem can therefore be written as

$$u = \sum_1^\infty J_0(\lambda_k r) \, e^{-\lambda_k^2 \, t} \, \frac{\displaystyle\int_0^1 r f(r) \, J_0(\lambda_k r) \, dr}{\frac{1}{2} \, J_1^2(\lambda_k)} \, .$$

To solve the reduced wave equation in spherical coordinates we write

$$u_{rr} + \frac{2}{r} u_r + \frac{1}{r^2 \sin \theta} \frac{\partial}{\partial \theta} \sin \theta \, u_\theta + \frac{1}{r^2 \sin^2 \theta} u_{\phi\phi} + k^2 u = 0$$

and apply the method of separation of variables. Then

$$u = R(r) \, P(\theta) \, E(\phi)$$

and we obtain

$$\left[\frac{r^2 R''(r)}{R(r)} + \frac{2r R'(r)}{R(r)} \right] + \left[\frac{1}{\sin \theta} \frac{\frac{\partial}{\partial \theta} \sin \theta \, P'(\theta)}{P(\theta)} \right] + \frac{1}{\sin^2 \theta} \left[\frac{E''(\phi)}{E(\phi)} \right] + r^2 k^2 = 0 \, .$$

We now introduce separation constants m and $n(n + 1)$ so that

$$\frac{E''}{E} = - m^2$$

$$\frac{1}{\sin \theta} \frac{\frac{d}{d\theta} \sin \theta \, P'(\theta)}{P(\theta)} - \frac{m^2}{\sin \theta} = - n(n + 1)$$

and

$$r^2 R''(r) + 2rR'(r) + [k^2 r^2 - m(n + 1)] R(r) = 0 \, .$$

The first two equations evidently have the solutions

$$E(\phi) = e^{\pm im\phi}$$

$$P(\theta) = P_n^m(\cos \theta).$$

The equation for $R(r)$ can be put into a more familiar form if we let $R(r) = J(r)/\sqrt{r}$. Then

$$J''(r) + \frac{1}{r} J(r) + \left[k^2 - \frac{\left(n + \frac{1}{2}\right)^2}{r^2} \right] J(r) = 0 \, .$$

This is Bessel's equation, whose solution can be written as $J_{n+1/2}(kr)$. We see that this time the index is no longer an integer but $n + \frac{1}{2}$, where n is an integer. This small change simplifies the picture somewhat. We can show, by direct substitution in the differential equation, that

$$J_{1/2}(kr) = \sqrt{\frac{2}{\pi kr}} \sin kr \, .$$

We can also derive the following formula,

$$\frac{J_{n+1/2}(kr)}{(kr)^{n+1/2}} = (-)^n \left(\frac{d}{k^2 r dr} \right)^n \frac{J_{1/2}(kr)}{\sqrt{kr}} \, ,$$

which is evidently related to

$$J_n(x) = (-)^n x^n \left(\frac{d}{x dx} \right)^n J_0(x) \, .$$

From it we see that

$$J_{n+1/2}(kr) = \frac{(-)^n r^{n+1/2}}{k^{n-1/2}} \left(\frac{d}{r dr} \right)^n \sqrt{\frac{2}{\pi}} \frac{\sin kr}{kr}$$

and evidently all these functions are expressible in terms of elementary functions.

Many of the properties derived in the previous sections can be applied to these functions as well. Thus the recurrence formula

$$J_{m+2}(x) - \frac{2(m+1)}{x} J_{m+1}(x) + J_m(x) = 0$$

holds for nonintegral values of m also.

The integral representation

$$J_m(x) = \frac{2}{\pi} \frac{x^m}{1 \times 3 \cdots (2m-1)} \int_0^{\pi/2} \sin^{2m} \psi \cos [x \cos \psi] \, d\psi$$

holds for nonintegral values of m, if one writes

$$1 \times 3 \cdots (2m-1) = \frac{(2m)!}{2^m m!} = \frac{\Gamma(2m+1)}{2^m \Gamma(m+1)}$$

(see note 5 Appendix to Chapter 1).

Then

$$J_m(x) = \frac{2}{\pi} \frac{(2x)^m \Gamma(m+1)}{\Gamma(2m+1)} \int_0^{\pi/2} \sin^{2m} \psi \cos [x \cos \psi] \, d\psi \, .$$

This can be simplified by applying the multiplication theorem of the Gamma function:

$$\Gamma(2m+1) = \frac{1}{\sqrt{2\pi}} 2^{2m+1/2} \Gamma\left(m + \frac{1}{2}\right) \Gamma(m+1)$$

to

$$J_m(x) = \frac{2\left(\frac{x}{2}\right)^m}{\sqrt{\pi} \, \Gamma\left(m + \frac{1}{2}\right)} \int_0^{\pi/2} \sin^{2m} \psi \cos [x \cos \psi] \, d\psi \, .$$

In particular for $m = n + 1/2$, where n is an integer, it becomes

$$J_{n+1/2}(x) = \frac{2\left(\frac{x}{2}\right)^{n+1/2}}{\sqrt{\pi} \, n!} \int_0^{\pi/2} \sin^{2n+1} \psi \cos [x \cos \psi] \, d\psi \, .$$

Similarly,

$$J_{m+1}(x) = \frac{x^{m+1}}{2^m \Gamma(m+1)} \int_0^{\pi/2} \sin \theta \cos^{2m+1} \theta \, J_0(x \sin \theta) \, d\theta$$

and

$$J_m(x) = \left(\frac{x}{2}\right)^m \sum_{k=0}^{\infty} \frac{\left(-\frac{x}{2}\right)^{2k}}{k! \, \Gamma(m+k+1)}$$

hold for nonintegral values of m.

8. The Complete Solution of Bessel's Equation

In the previous section we have discussed only the one solution of Bessel's equation that is known as the Bessel function. But a second-order differential equation has two linearly independent solutions.

We now examine the series

$$J_m(x) = \left(\frac{x}{2}\right)^m \sum_{k=0}^{\infty} \frac{\left(-\frac{x}{2}\right)^{2k}}{k!\,\Gamma(m+k+1)}$$

and observe that only the term m^2 enters the differential equation. Therefore, replacing m by $-m$ leaves the equation unchanged and thus

$$J_{-m}(x) = \left(\frac{x}{2}\right)^{-m} \sum_{k=0}^{\infty} \frac{\left(-\frac{x}{2}\right)^{2k}}{k!\,\Gamma(-m+k+1)}$$

is a second solution. But this is true only for nonintegral values of m. For integral m we saw earlier that

$$J_{-m}(x) = (-1)^m J_m(x),$$

which can also be derived from the infinite series and properties of the Gamma function. Thus for integral m, $J_m(x)$ and $J_{-m}(x)$ are not independent solutions.

Sometimes another solution is used, which is known as Neumann's function and defined by

$$N_v(x) = \frac{\cos v\pi \; J_v(x) - J_{-v}(x)}{\sin v\pi}.$$

When v is not integral this is a solution that is independent of $J_v(x)$. When v approaches an integer m, the term on the right becomes indeterminate, but one can now show that

$$N_m(x) = \lim_{v \to m} \frac{\cos v\pi \; J_v(x) - J_{-v}(x)}{\sin v\pi}$$

is a solution that is independent of $J_m(x)$.

Another set of solutions, which are of value in certain applications, are the Hankel functions defined by

$$H_v^{(1)}(x) = J_v(x) + i\,N_v(x)$$

$$H_v^{(2)}(x) = J_v(x) - i\,N_v(x).$$

Exercises

1. Show by direct substitution that the series for $J_m(x)$ derived in Section 3 is a solution of Bessel's equation.

2. Show that

$$\sum_0^\infty \frac{r^n P_n(\cos \theta)}{n!} = e^{r \cos \theta} J_0(r \sin \theta) .$$

3. Show that the general solution of

$$y'' + \frac{9}{4} ty = 0$$

is given by

$$y = At^{1/2} J_{1/3}(t^{3/2}) + Bt^{1/2} J_{-1/3}(t^{3/2}) .$$

4. Show that

$$\cos (t \sin \theta) = J_0(t) + 2 \sum_{k=1}^\infty J_{2k}(t) \cos 2k \, \theta$$

$$\sin (t \sin \theta) = 2 \sum_{k=0}^\infty J_{2k+1}(t) \sin (2k + 1) \, \theta .$$

5. Show that

$$J_0^2 (t) + 2 \sum_1^\infty J_n^2(t) = 1 .$$

6. Use the integral representation on page 47 to show that

$$\sum_{n=0}^\infty \frac{J_n(x) \, t^n}{n!} = J_0\left(\sqrt{x^2 - 2xt}\right) .$$

7. Show that

$$J_m(x) = \frac{2^m m!}{(2m)!} x^m \left(1 + \frac{d^2}{dx^2}\right)^m J_0(x) .$$

8. Show, using the methods of Section 7, that

$$1 = - 2 \sum_{k=1}^\infty \frac{J_0(\lambda_k x)}{\lambda_k J_0'(\lambda_k)} = 2 \sum_1^\infty \frac{J_0(\lambda_k x)}{\lambda_k J_1(\lambda_k)} ,$$

where $J_0(\lambda_k) = 0$.

9. Show that

$$\int_0^\infty e^{-st}\, J_m(t)\, dt = \frac{1}{\sqrt{1+s^2}\,\left[s+\sqrt{1+s^2}\right]^m}$$

$$\int_0^\infty e^{-st}\, \frac{J_m(t)}{t}\, dt = \frac{1}{m\left(s+\sqrt{1+s^2}\right)^m}\,.$$

10. Use the previous result to show that

$$n\int_0^t J_m(t-\tau)\,\frac{J_n(\tau)}{\tau}d\tau = J_{m+n}(t)\,.$$

11. It was shown that

$$J_0(x) = \sum_{k=0}^\infty \frac{\left(-\dfrac{x}{2}\right)^{2k}}{k!^2}\,.$$

Since $J_0(x)$ has an infinity of zeros $\pm\lambda_1, \pm\lambda_2$, it should be possible to factor $J_0(x)$ into the infinite product

$$J_0(x) = \prod_{k=1}^\infty \left(1-\frac{x^2}{\lambda_k^2}\right)\,.$$

(Under what conditions do such products converge?)
Use this result to show that

$$\sum_1^\infty \frac{1}{\lambda_k^2} = \frac{1}{4}\,, \qquad \sum_1^\infty \frac{1}{\lambda_k^4} = \frac{1}{32}\,.$$

[4]

Mathieu Functions

1. Introduction

In the previous two chapters we observed that if one applies the method of separation of variables to the wave equation one is led to a set of ordinary differential equations. In the application it was necessary to introduce certain constants known as separation constants. At first these constants are completely arbitrary. But if one then takes into consideration the boundary values and regularity conditions imposed by the physical situation one finds that these separation constants must belong to an infinite but discrete set of numbers. This general approach is applicable in a number of coordinate systems, and in this chapter we will study the wave equation in elliptic cylinder coordinates.

The elliptic cylinder coordinates (ξ, η, z) can be related to the rectangular coordinates by the equations

$$x = c \cosh \xi \cos \eta$$

$$y = c \sinh \xi \sin \eta$$

$$z = z,$$

where c is an arbitrary real parameter. The coordinates lie in the intervals $0 \leq \xi < \infty$, $0 \leq \eta \leq 2\pi$, and $-\infty < z < \infty$. The surface $\xi = \xi_0$ represents an elliptic cylinder

$$\frac{x^2}{c^2 \cosh^2 \xi_0} + \frac{y^2}{c^2 \sinh^2 \xi_0} = 1$$

and the surface $\eta = \eta_0$ is defined by

$$\frac{x^2}{c^2 \cos^2 \eta_0} - \frac{y^2}{c^2 \sin^2 \eta_0} = 1 \, .$$

The wave equation, when expressed in this coordinate system, becomes

$$\frac{\partial^2 u}{\partial \xi^2} + \frac{\partial^2 u}{\partial \eta^2} + \frac{c^2}{2} (\cosh 2\xi - \cos 2\eta) \frac{\partial^2 u}{\partial z^2} + k^2 \frac{c^2}{2} (\cosh 2\xi - \cos 2\eta) u = 0 \, .$$

We now assume that a solution u of the form

$$u = M(\xi) \, m(\eta) \, Z(z)$$

59

can be found, and we insert that into the equation. In accordance with the method of separation of variables we then obtain three ordinary differential equations

$$\frac{d^2M(\xi)}{d\xi^2} + \left[-\lambda + \frac{c^2}{2}(k^2 - \alpha^2)\cosh 2\xi\right] M(\xi) = 0$$

$$\frac{d^2m(\eta)}{d\eta^2} + \left[\lambda - \frac{c^2}{2}(k^2 - \alpha^2)\cos 2\eta\right] m(\eta) = 0$$

$$\frac{d^2Z(z)}{dz^2} + \alpha^2 Z(z) = 0\,.$$

The last of these equations is the familiar harmonic equation. The first and second are known as the modified Mathieu equation and the Mathieu equation, respectively. These two are very closely related. If one uses the substitution $\xi = i\eta$, the first is converted into the second. In this chapter we will concern ourselves exclusively with the second of these equations and write it in the standard form

$$y''(t) + \left[\lambda - 2h^2\cos 2t\right] y(t) = 0.$$

2. General Properties of Mathieu Functions

The Mathieu equation

$$y''(t) + \left[\lambda - 2h^2\cos 2t\right] y(t) = 0$$

is somewhat different from the second-order linear differential equations, which were studied in the previous chapters. There the coefficients were algebraic functions of the independent variable, whereas in the Mathieu equation the coefficients are periodic functions. From the physical situation we see that in terms of the elliptic coordinates (ξ, η, z) we expect u, the solution of the wave equation, to be a periodic function of η, of period 2π. We therefore raise the question of under what conditions will

$$y(t + 2\pi) = y(t).$$

The equation contains two parameters, λ and h, which so far are arbitrary. But we expect the restriction of periodicity to impose some restriction of the parameters. For example, when $h = 0$ we see that

$$y = c_1 \cos \sqrt{\lambda}\, t + c_2 \sin \sqrt{\lambda}\, t$$

and in order for y to have period 2π it is necessary that

$$\sqrt{\lambda} = n\pi\,,$$

where n is an integer.

We will now consider the more general equation

$$y'' + \Phi(t)y = 0 \,,$$

where $\Phi(t)$ is an even, periodic real function of period π. In the case of the Mathieu equation, evidently,

$$\Phi(t) = \lambda - 2h^2 \cos 2t \,.$$

This more general equation was first studied by the astronomer G. W. Hill and is called Hill's equation.

First we shall construct two normalized solutions y_1 and y_2 defined by the initial values

$$y_1(0) = 1, \qquad y_2(0) = 0$$
$$y_1'(0) = 0, \qquad y_2'(0) = 1.$$

That such solutions exist follows from the theory of differential equations. In particular, in the case of the Mathieu equation, for $h = 0$

$$y_1 = \cos \sqrt{\lambda}\, t \,, \qquad y_2 = \frac{\sin \sqrt{\lambda}\, t}{\sqrt{\lambda}} \,.$$

Under the substitution of variables $\tau = t + \pi$, the equation remains unchanged because of the periodicity of $\Phi(t)$. Then $y_1(t + \pi)$ and $y_2(t + \pi)$ must also be solutions, and any solution can be expressed as a linear combination of y_1 and y_2. Since $y_1(t + \pi)$ has the initial values $y_1(\pi)$ and $y_1'(\pi)$, and similarly $y_2(t + \pi)$ has the initial values $y_2(\pi)$ and $y_2'(\pi)$, we find that

$$y_1(t + \pi) = y_1(\pi)\, y_1(t) + y_1'(\pi)\, y_2(t)$$
$$y_2(t + \pi) = y_2(\pi)\, y_1(t) + y_2'(\pi)\, y_2(t).$$

The expression $y_1(t)\, y_2'(t) - y_2(t)\, y_1'(t)$ is known as the Wronskian of y_1 and y_2. We can easily show that in this case it is a constant:

$$w(t) = y_1(t)\, y_2'(t) - y_2(t)\, y_1'(t)$$
$$w'(t) = y_1(t)\, y_2''(t) - y_2(t)\, y_1''(t)$$
$$= - y_1(t)\, \Phi(t)\, y_2(t) + y_2(t)\, \Phi(t)\, y_1(t) = 0.$$

Thus $w(t) = c$, and from the initial values it follows that $w(t) = 1$. Thus we see that

$$w(\pi) = y_1(\pi)\, y_2'(\pi) - y_2(\pi)\, y_1'(\pi) = 1.$$

In general, we certainly cannot expect the solutions of the differential equation to be periodic. But we can find solutions with the property that

$$y(t + \pi) = \rho y(t)$$

for some constant ρ.

To find such a solution we take some linear combination of y_1 and y_2—say

$$y(t) = c_1 y_1(t) + c_2 y_2(t),$$

and demand that

$$y(t + \pi) = \rho y(t).$$

This leads to the equation

$$c_1 y_1(t + \pi) + c_2 y_2(t + \pi) = \rho[c_1 y_1(t) + c_2 y_2(t)],$$

which can be put into the form

$$c_1[y_1(\pi) y_1(t) + y_1'(\pi) y_2(t)] + c_2[y_2(\pi) y_1(t) + y_2'(\pi) y_2(t)] = \rho[c_1 y_1(t) + c_2 y_2(t)].$$

Since y_1 and y_2 are linearly independent solutions, the coefficients of y_1 on both sides of the equation must match, and similarly for the coefficients of y_2. We thus obtain the following system of equations for c_1 and c_2:

$$c_1[y_1(\pi) - \rho] + c_2 y_2(\pi) = 0$$
$$c_1 y_1'(\pi) + c_2[y_2'(\pi) - \rho] = 0.$$

This is a homogeneous system and can have nonzero solutions if and only if the determinant of the system vanishes. That is,

$$\begin{vmatrix} y_1(\pi) - \rho & y_2(\pi) \\ y_1'(\pi) & y_2'(\pi) - \rho \end{vmatrix} = 0.$$

Expansion of the determinant leads to a quadratic equation for ρ:

$$\rho^2 - [y_1(\pi) + y_2'(\pi)] \rho + y_1(\pi) y_2'(\pi) - y_1'(\pi) y_2(\pi) = 0.$$

Use of the fact that $w(\pi) = 1$ allows us to simplify the equation to read

$$\rho^2 - [y_1(\pi) + y_2'(\pi)] \rho + 1 = 0.$$

The last equation has, in general, two different roots, ρ_1 and ρ_2, corresponding to each of which we can find a set of coefficients c_1 and c_2, which gives us two solutions of the differential equation,—say $u_1(t)$ and $u_2(t)$—such that

$$u_1(t + \pi) = \rho_1 u_1(t)$$
$$u_2(t + \pi) = \rho_2 u_2(t).$$

We must here distinguish between three distinct cases:

$$| y_1(\pi) + y_2'(\pi) | \begin{array}{l} < 2 \\ = 2 \\ > 2. \end{array}$$

In the first case, where

$$| y_1(\pi) + y_2'(\pi) | < 2,$$

we see from the quadratic equation that ρ_1 and ρ_2 are complex numbers of absolute value 1. Then u_1 and u_2 are solutions whose absolute value is bounded and therefore all solutions are bounded. We say in this case that all solutions are stable. On the other hand, in the third case, where

$$| y_1(\pi) + y_2'(\pi) | > 2,$$

ρ_1 and ρ_2 are real and since $\rho_1\rho_2 = 1$, at least one must be greater than 1 in absolute value. Then if

$$| \rho_1 | < 1, \qquad | \rho_2 | > 1,$$

we see that u_1 is a bounded and u_2 an unbounded solution. The second case breaks down into two subcases

$$y_1(\pi) + y_2'(\pi) = \pm 2.$$

When $y_1(\pi) + y_2'(\pi) = 2$ we have only one double root, $\rho = 1$. Similarly, when $y_1(\pi) + y_2'(\pi) = -2$ there is a double root $\rho = -1$. In either of these cases we can in general expect only one solution with the property

$$y(t + \pi) = \rho y(t),$$

although in exceptional cases there may be two such solutions. For $\rho = 1$ we can find a solution of period π—that is

$$y(t + \pi) = y(t).$$

For $\rho = -1$ the solution has period 2π, since

$$y(t + 2\pi) = - 1y(t + \pi) = y(t).$$

In a search for periodic solutions we can restrict ourselves to purely even or odd solutions. Since the differential equation is unchanged if t is replaced by $-t$ it follows that, if $y(t)$ is a solution, so is $y(-t)$. Therefore, unless $y(t)$ is even or odd, $y(-t)$ will be independent of $y(t)$. By a suitable choice of multiplier of $y(t)$, we can insure the condition $y(0) = 1$. Then evidently

$$y_1(t) = \frac{y(t) + y(-t)}{2}, \quad y_2(t) = \frac{y(t) - y(-t)}{2}$$

since the functions on the right have the same initial conditions as $y_1(t)$ and $y_2(t)$. Now if $y(t)$ has period π or 2π, so do $y_1(t)$ and $y_2(t)$. Of course, when $y(t)$ is even to begin with it is $y_1(t)$ and

$$y(t) - y(-t) \equiv 0.$$

Similarly, if $y(t)$ is odd it is $y_2(t)$ and

$$y(t) + y(-t) \equiv 0.$$

We now suppose that $y_1(t)$ is an even periodic solution of period π, so that

$$y_1(t + \pi) = y_1(t)$$

and also

$$y_1'(t + \pi) = y_1'(t).$$

Since $y_1(t)$ is even $y_1'(t)$ is odd. Then we have for $t = -\pi/2$

$$y_1'\left(\frac{\pi}{2}\right) = y_1'\left(-\frac{\pi}{2}\right) = -y_1'\left(\frac{\pi}{2}\right),$$

from which we draw the conclusion that

$$y_1'\left(\frac{\pi}{2}\right) = 0.$$

Conversely, we can show that if $y_1'(\pi/2) = 0$ then $y_1(t)$ is necessarily periodic of period π. We see that $y_1(t + \pi)$ satisfies Mathieu's equation so that

$$y_1(t + \pi) = c_1 y_1(t) + c_2 y_2(t)$$

and by differentiation

$$y_1'(t + \pi) = c_1 y_1'(t) + c_2 y_2'(t).$$

To find c_1 and c_2 we let $t = -\pi/2$ and observe that $y_1(t)$ and $y_2'(t)$ are even, and $y_1'(t)$ and $y_2(t)$ are odd. Then

$$y_1\left(\frac{\pi}{2}\right) = c_1 y_1\left(\frac{\pi}{2}\right) - c_2 y_2\left(\frac{\pi}{2}\right)$$

$$y_1'\left(\frac{\pi}{2}\right) = -c_1 y_1'\left(\frac{\pi}{2}\right) + c_2 y_2'\left(\frac{\pi}{2}\right).$$

At a point where $y_1'(t)$ vanishes, $y_2'(t)$ cannot vanish. Otherwise, $y_2(t)$ would be a multiple of $y_1(t)$. Therefore, if $y_1'(\pi/2) = 0$, the second of the above equations tells us that $c_2 = 0$, and the first equation shows that $c_1 = 1$. Thus

$$y_1(t + \pi) = y_1(t).$$

We can now state that there exists a nontrivial periodic solution that is

(1) even and of period π
    if and only if $y_1'(\pi/2) = 0$

(2) odd and of period π
    if and only if $y_2(\pi/2) = 0$

(3) even and of period 2π
    if and only if $y_1(\pi/2) = 0$

(4) odd and of period 2π
    if and only if $y_2'(\pi/2) = 0$.

Case *(1)* was proved in detail and the three other cases can be proved by analogous arguments.

3. Particular Properties of Mathieu Functions

The Mathieu equation

$$y'' + [\lambda - 2h^2 \cos 2t]\, y = 0$$

will have an even periodic solution of period π if and only if

$$y_1'\left(\frac{\pi}{2}\right) = 0.$$

But $y_1(t)$ is a solution of the equation with initial conditions

$$y_1(0) = 1, \qquad y_1'(0) = 0.$$

Since λ and h^2 appear in the equation, $y_1(t)$ will also be a function of λ and h^2. This fact will be emphasized by writing $y_1(t; \lambda, h^2)$. Thus the condition

$$y_1'\left(\frac{\pi}{2}; \lambda, h^2\right) = 0$$

imposes certain restrictions on λ and h^2. What is more, this condition implies that λ can be considered as a function of h^2, which will be indicated by writing $\lambda(h^2)$. The explicit construction of this function is impossible in terms of elementary functions and the numerical evaluation for specific values of h^2 is very tedious, except for $h^2 = 0$. In this case we evidently have

$$y_1[t; \lambda(0), 0] = \cos \sqrt{\lambda(0)}\; t$$

and

$$y_1'\left(\frac{\pi}{2}; \lambda(0), 0\right) = -\sqrt{\lambda(0)} \sin \sqrt{\lambda(0)}\; \frac{\pi}{2} = 0.$$

Thus it is necessary that

$$\lambda(0) = 4n^2,$$

where n is an arbitrary integer. Since n is arbitrary we see that there must be an infinity of functions $\lambda_0(h^2)$, $\lambda_2(h^2)$, $\cdots$ such that

$$y_1'\left[\frac{\pi}{2}; \lambda_{2n}(h^2), h^2\right] = 0$$

and $\lambda_{2n}(0) = 4n^2$.

Thus we see that the equation

$$y'' + [\lambda_{2n}(h^2) - 2h^2 \cos 2t]\, y = 0$$

has an even periodic solution of period π, which is usually denoted by the symbol $ce_{2n}(t)$. Every periodic function can be represented by a Fourier series.

In particular if the function is even and of period π, only Fourier terms of the form cos $2rt$ are required. Thus it must be possible to find such an expansion for $ce_{2n}(t)$. Then

$$ce_{2n}(t) = \sum_{r=0}^{\infty} A_{2n,2r} \cos 2rt \ .$$

To determine the coefficients $A_{2n,2r}$ we insert the Fourier series in the differential equation

$$-\sum_{r=0}^{\infty} 4r^2 A_{2n,2r} \cos 2rt + \lambda_{2n}(h^2) \sum_{r=0}^{\infty} A_{2n,2r} \cos 2rt$$

$$- 2h^2 \sum_{r=0}^{\infty} A_{2n,2r} \cos 2t \cos 2rt = 0 \ .$$

By a trigonometric identity the product of cosines in the last summation can be written as a sum, so that

$$-\sum_{r=0}^{\infty} [4r^2 - \lambda_{2n}(h^2)] A_{2n,2r} \cos 2rt - h^2 \sum_{r=0}^{\infty} A_{2n,2r} [\cos (2r - 2)t$$

$$+ \cos (2r + 2)t] = 0 \ .$$

By a rearrangement of terms the equation can be rewritten as a simple Fourier series:

$$\left[\lambda_{2n}(h^2) A_{2n,0} - h^2 A_{2n,2}\right] - \left[[4 - \lambda_{2n}(h^2)] A_{2n,2} + h^2(2A_{2n,0} + A_{2n,4})\right] \cos 2t$$

$$- \sum_{r=2}^{\infty} \left[[4r^2 - \lambda_{2n}(h^2)] A_{2n,2r} + h^2(A_{2n,2r+2} + A_{2n,2r-2})\right] \cos 2rt = 0.$$

A Fourier series can vanish only if every Fourier coefficient vanishes. Thus we obtain the following system of equations:

$$\lambda_{2n}(h^2) A_{2n,0} - h^2 A_{2n,2} = 0$$

$$2h^2 A_{2n,0} + [4 - \lambda_{2n}(h^2)] A_{2n,2} + h^2 A_{2n,4} = 0$$

$$h^2 A_{2n,2r-2} + [4r^2 - \lambda_{2n}(h^2)] A_{2n,2r} + h^2 A_{2n,2r+2} = 0, \qquad r = 2, 3, \cdots .$$

The above is an infinite system of linear equations for the Fourier coefficients $A_{2n,2r}$. One obvious solution is the trivial solution, all $A_{2n,2r} = 0$. But a homogeneous system of this type will also have nontrivial solutions, provided the determinant of the system vanishes.

Before writing down the determinant of the system we will divide the second equation by 4 and the succeeding ones by $4r^2$. Then we obtain a system of equations, whose determinant is

$$
\begin{vmatrix}
\lambda & -h^2 & 0 & 0 & 0 & \cdots \\
\dfrac{2h^2}{4} & 1 - \dfrac{\lambda}{4} & \dfrac{h^2}{4} & 0 & 0 & \cdots \\
0 & \dfrac{h^2}{16} & 1 - \dfrac{\lambda}{16} & \dfrac{h^2}{16} & 0 & \cdots \\
0 & 0 & \dfrac{h^2}{36} & 1 - \dfrac{\lambda}{36} & \dfrac{h^2}{36} & \cdots \\
0 & 0 & 0 & \dfrac{h^2}{64} & 1 - \dfrac{\lambda}{64} & \\
\vdots & \vdots & \vdots & \vdots & \vdots & \ddots
\end{vmatrix} = 0 .
$$

This determinant is infinite, but one can show that infinite determinants do converge to specific values under certain conditions. These are satisfied in this case. One can see this intuitively, by observing that the diagonal elements approach 1 in the limit and the off-diagonal elements approach 0. This is a relationship between λ and h^2, and therefore will determine λ as a function of h^2. Evidently the values of λ satisfying the determinant must be the same as those satisfying the equation

$$
y_1'\left(\frac{\pi}{2}; \lambda, h^2\right) = 0 .
$$

But one can use the determinant to obtain approximate values for $\lambda_{2n}(h^2)$. For example, we approximate the determinant by the truncated third-order determinant

$$
\begin{vmatrix}
\lambda & -h^2 & 0 \\
\dfrac{2h^2}{4} & 1 - \dfrac{\lambda}{4} & \dfrac{h^2}{4} \\
0 & \dfrac{h^2}{16} & 1 - \dfrac{\lambda}{16}
\end{vmatrix} = 0 .
$$

Then we find

$$
\lambda_0(h^2) \approx -\frac{1}{2}h^4 + \frac{7}{128}h^8 + \cdots
$$

$$
\lambda_2(h^2) \approx 4 + \frac{5}{12}h^4 + \cdots
$$

$$
\lambda_4(h^2) \approx 16 + \cdots .
$$

More precise formulas are obtained by taking higher order determinants. Now it is possible to return to the recurrence relations defining the coefficients $A_{2n,2r}$, and for $n = 0$ we find, assuming $A_{0,0} = 1$,

$$ce_0(t) = 1 + \left(-\frac{1}{2}h^2 + \frac{7}{128}h^6 + \cdots\right)\cos 2t + \left(\frac{1}{32}h^4 + \cdots\right)\cos 4t + \cdots.$$

Another method of finding $\lambda_{2n}(h^2)$ as well as $ce_{2n}(t)$ is to assume that expansions exist of the form

$$\lambda_{2n}(h^2) = 4n^2 + \sum_{k=1}^{\infty} c_k h^{2k}$$

$$ce_{2n}(t) = \sum_{k=0}^{\infty} y_k(t)\, h^{2k}\,.$$

These expansions are then inserted in the differential equation and coefficients of powers of h^{2k} are equated to zero. This leads to an infinite system of ordinary differential equations for the functions $y_k(t)$. In order that all of them be periodic it will be necessary to impose certain conditions on the coefficients c_k, so that $\lambda_{2n}(h^2)$ as well as $ce_{2n}(t)$ are determined. We shall illustrate this process for the case $n = 1$. Let

$$\lambda_2(h^2) = 4 + \sum_{k=1}^{\infty} c_k h^{2k}$$

$$ce_2(t) = \sum_{k=0}^{\infty} y_k(t)\, h^{2k}\,.$$

Then we obtain, by inserting these expressions in Mathieu's equation,

$$\sum_{k=0}^{\infty} y_k''(t)\, h^{2k} + \left(4 + \sum_{k=1}^{\infty} c_k h^{2k}\right)\sum_{k=0}^{\infty} y_k(t)\, h^{2k} - 2\sum_{k=0}^{\infty}\cos 2t\, y_k(t)\, h^{2k+2} = 0\,.$$

One can rearrange the equation to obtain the form

$$\sum_{k=0}^{\infty} h^{2k}\left[y_k''(t) + 4y_k(t) + \sum_{l=1}^{k} c_l y_{k-l}(t) - 2\cos 2t\, y_{k-1}(t)\right] = 0\,,$$

where $\sum_{l=1}^{k} c_l y_{k-l}(t) = 0$ for $k = 0$.

Since every coefficient of h^{2k} must vanish we obtain the following system of differential equations:

$$y_0''(t) + 4y_0(t) = 0$$
$$y_1''(t) + 4y_1(t) = 2\cos 2t\, y_0(t) - c_1 y_0(t)$$
$$y_2''(t) + 4y_2(t) = 2\cos 2t\, y_1(t) - c_1 y_1(t) - c_2 y_0(t).$$
$$\vdots$$

All $y_k(t)$ should be even functions of period π. Then we see from the first of the above equations that

$$y_0(t) = \cos 2t.$$

Using this value of $y_0(t)$ we can solve the second equation, and we find that

$$y_1(t) = \frac{1}{3} \frac{\cos 4t}{12} - c_1 \frac{t \sin 2t}{4}.$$

Evidently $y_1(t)$ will not be periodic unless $c_1 = 0$. If we impose this condition we have

$$y_1(t) = \frac{1}{4} - \frac{\cos 4t}{12}.$$

Now we can solve the third equation using the values of $y_0(t)$, $y_1(t)$, and c_1 found so far and we obtain

$$y_2(t) = \left(\frac{5}{48} - \frac{c_2}{4}\right)t \sin 2t + \frac{\cos 6t}{384}.$$

In order for $y_2(t)$ to be periodic we require that the coefficient of $t \sin 2t$ vanishes, so that $c_2 = 5/12$. Thus we find

$$ce_2(t) = \cos 2t + h^2\left(\frac{1}{4} - \frac{\cos 4t}{12}\right) + h^4 \frac{\cos 6t}{384} + \cdots$$

$$\lambda_2(h^2) = 4 + \frac{5}{12}h^4 + \cdots.$$

The above process can evidently be carried out any number of times to obtain as many terms as are desired.

So far we have considered only the first of the four cases discussed in Section 2. But evidently the same methods can be applied to the other three cases. We can thus see that there are four distinct types of periodic solutions. These four cases are as follows:

(1) $ce_{2n}(t) = \sum\limits_{r=0}^{\infty} A_{2n,2r} \cos 2rt$

is even, has period π, and satisfies the boundary condition

$$y_1'\left(\frac{\pi}{2}\right) = 0.$$

(2) $se_{2n}(t) = \sum\limits_{r=1}^{\infty} B_{2n,2r} \sin 2rt$

is odd, has period π, and satisfies the boundary condition

$$y_2\left(\frac{\pi}{2}\right) = 0.$$

(3) $ce_{2n+1}(t) = \sum\limits_{r=0}^{\infty} A_{2n+1,2r+1} \cos{(2r+1)t}$

is even, has period 2π, and satisfies the boundary condition

$$y_1\left(\frac{\pi}{2}\right) = 0 .$$

(4) $se_{2n+1}(t) = \sum\limits_{r=0}^{\infty} B_{2n+1,2r+1} \sin{(2r+1)t}$

is odd, has period 2π, and satisfies the boundary condition

$$y_2'\left(\frac{\pi}{2}\right) = 0 .$$

In order for the Mathieu equation to have one of these solutions, λ will have to be some particular function of h^2. We will denote these values, for the four cases, as follows:

(1) $\lambda_{2n}(n^2) = (2n)^2 + \cdots$

(2) $\lambda_{2n+1}(h^2) = (2n+2)^2 + \cdots$

(3) $\lambda'_{2n+1}(h^2) = (2n+1)^2 + \cdots$

(4) $\lambda'_{2n+2}(h^2) = (2n+1)^2 + \cdots .$

Thus, for example, the equation

$$y'' + \left[\lambda'_{2n+1}(h^2) - 2h^2 \cos 2t\right] y = 0$$

has the periodic solution

$$y = ce_{2n+1}(t).$$

It is evident that for h^2 sufficiently small but not zero,

$$\lambda_{2n} < \lambda'_{2n+1} < \lambda_{2n+1}$$

$$\lambda_{2n} < \lambda'_{2n+2} < \lambda_{2n+1}.$$

By a more delicate analysis one can show that for all $h^2 > 0$,

$$\lambda_0 < \lambda'_1 < \lambda'_2 < \lambda_1 < \lambda_2 < \lambda'_3 < \lambda'_4 < \lambda_3 < \lambda_4 < \cdots .$$

The fact that there are no equality signs in the above sequence is highly significant. The implication of this statement is that for none of the λ's in that sequence can the Mathieu equation have more than one periodic solution. That is, in each of the four cases discussed the second solution of the differential equation is not periodic. The proof of this statement is surprisingly simple.

First we shall show that for no one value of λ can we obtain two solutions of the type $ce_{2n}(t)$ and $se_{2k+1}(t)$. We know that the Wronskian of two independent solutions of the Mathieu equation is a nonzero constant. That is,

$$ce_{2n}(t) \frac{d}{dt} se_{2k+1}(t) - se_{2k+1}(t) \frac{d}{dt} ce_{2n}(t) = \text{constant} \neq 0 .$$

But the first term on the left is an even function and the second term is an odd function. The difference between an even and an odd function can be constant only if both are constant functions, which is patently not true in this case. Thus we cannot have a Mathieu equation with solutions of the types $ce_{2n}(t)$ and $se_{2k+1}(t)$.

Now we shall show that no Mathieu equation can have two solutions of the types $ce_{2n}(t)$ and $se_{2k}(t)$. We saw that if we express $ce_{2n}(t)$ as a Fourier series

$$ce_{2n}(t) = \sum_{r=0}^{\infty} A_{2n,2r} \cos 2rt$$

then the Fourier coefficients must satisfy the equations

$$\lambda A_{2n,0} - h^2 A_{2n,2} = 0$$

$$2h^2 A_{2n,0} + (4 - \lambda) A_{2n,2} + h^2 A_{2n,4} = 0$$

$$h^2 A_{2n,2r-2} + (4r^2 - \lambda) A_{2n,2r} + h^2 A_{2n,2r+2} = 0$$

$$r = 2, 3, \cdots .$$

Similarly, if we express $se_{2k}(t)$ as a Fourier series we obtain

$$se_{2k}(t) = \sum_{r=1}^{\infty} B_{2k,2r} \sin 2rt ,$$

where

$$(4 - \lambda) B_{2k,2} + h^2 B_{2k,4} = 0$$

$$h^2 B_{2k,2r-2} + (4r^2 - \lambda) B_{2k,2r} + h^2 B_{2k,2r+2} = 0,$$

$$r = 2, 3, \cdots .$$

We now consider the following family of determinants,

$$u_r = \begin{vmatrix} B_{2k,2r} & A_{2n,2r} \\ B_{2k,2r+2} & A_{2n,2r+2} \end{vmatrix} , \qquad r = 2, 3, \cdots .$$

By use of the above recurrence relationships we can rewrite the determinant in the form

$$
u_r = \begin{vmatrix} B_{2k,2r} & A_{2n,2r} \\[2em] -B_{2k,2r-2} - \dfrac{(4r^2-\lambda)}{h^2} B_{2k,2r} & -A_{2n,2r-2} - \dfrac{(4r^2-\lambda)}{h^2} A_{2n,2r} \end{vmatrix}
$$

$$
= \begin{vmatrix} B_{2k,2r} & A_{2n,2r} \\[1em] -B_{2k,2r-2} & -A_{2n,2r-2} \end{vmatrix} = \begin{vmatrix} B_{2k,2r-2} & A_{2n,2r-2} \\[1em] B_{2k,2r} & A_{2n,2r} \end{vmatrix} = u_{r-1} .
$$

Thus we see that

$$
u_r = u_{r-1} = \cdots = u_2 ,
$$

so that all determinants are equal. We can express u_2 very simply in terms of $A_{2n,0}$ and $B_{2k,2}$ since

$$
u_2 = \begin{vmatrix} B_{2k,2} & A_{2n,2} \\[1em] B_{2k,4} & A_{2n,1} \end{vmatrix} = \begin{vmatrix} B_{2k,2} & A_{2n,2} \\[1em] -\dfrac{(4-\lambda)}{n^2} B_{2k,2} & -2A_{2n,0} - \dfrac{(4-\lambda)}{h^2} A_{2n,2} \end{vmatrix}
$$

$$
= \begin{vmatrix} B_{2k,2} & A_{2n,2} \\[1em] 0 & -2A_{2n,0} \end{vmatrix} = -2A_{2n,0} B_{2k,2} .
$$

We see that $A_{2n,0}$ cannot vanish, for otherwise all $A_{2n,2k}$ would vanish, as shown by the recurrence relationships. Similarly, $B_{2k,2}$ cannot vanish. But to insure the convergence of the Fourier series we require that

$$
\lim_{r \to \infty} A_{2n,2r} = \lim_{r \to \infty} B_{2k,2r} = 0 ,
$$

which implies that

$$
\lim_{r \to \infty} u_r = 0 .
$$

But we have just shown that u_r is a nonzero constant. Therefore our original assumption that a Mathieu equation had two solutions of the types $ce_{2n}(t)$ and $se_{2k}(t)$ must be false.

By a repetition of these considerations with the remaining combinations of the four types of periodic solutions we can complete the proof that for no one value of λ can two periodic solutions of a Mathieu equation coexist.

4. Stability Criteria

In Section 2 it was shown that when

$$| y_1(\pi; \lambda, h^2) + y_2'(\pi; \lambda, h^2) | < 2$$

all solutions of the Mathieu equation are bounded; when

$$| y_1(\pi; \lambda, h^2) + y_2'(\pi; \lambda, h^2) | > 2$$

one solution is unbounded; when

$$y_1(\pi; \lambda, h^2) + y_2'(\pi; \lambda, h^2) = 2$$

one solution has period π; and when

$$y_1(\pi; \lambda, h^2) + y_2'(\pi; \lambda, h^2) = -2$$

one solution has period 2π.

Evidently the values of λ for which

$$y_1(\pi; \lambda, h^2) + y_2'(\pi; \lambda, h^2) = 2$$

must be those λ_n determined in Section 3, for which solutions of period π exist. Similarly, the equation

$$y_1(\pi; \lambda, h^2) + y_2'(\pi; \lambda, h^2) = -2$$

must have the roots λ_n', for which solutions of period 2π exist.

For $\lambda < \lambda_0$ we expect one solution to be unbounded. This is evident if we take λ very small—say $-l^2$, where l is large so that

$$y'' - (l^2 + 2h^2 \cos 2t)y = 0;$$

and if l is large relative to h we have

$$y_1(t) \approx \cosh lt$$
$$y_2(t) \approx \sinh lt.$$

Then

$$y_1(\pi) + y_2'(\pi) \approx (1 + l) \cosh l\pi > 2$$

for large l. We shall use the abbreviation

$$z(\lambda) = y_1(\pi) + y_2'(\pi)$$

and observe how $z(\lambda)$ varies as λ increases from $-\infty$ to $+\infty$. It can then be shown that for

$(-\infty, \lambda_0)$	$z(\lambda) > 2$
(λ_0, λ_1')	$-2 < z(\lambda) < 2$
(λ_2', λ_1')	$z(\lambda) < -2$
(λ_2', λ_1)	$-2 < z(\lambda) < 2$
(λ_1, λ_2)	$z(\lambda) > 2$

$$\vdots$$

We can then state that if λ lies in one of the intervals

$$(\lambda_0, \lambda_1'), \quad (\lambda_2', \lambda_1), \quad (\lambda_2, \lambda_3'), \quad (\lambda_4', \lambda_3), \quad \cdots$$

all solutions of the Mathieu equation are bounded. For λ's outside of these intervals one solution is unbounded, and at the end points one solution is periodic with period π or 2π. The above intervals are called the stability intervals.

5. Expansion and Orthogonality Properties

The four types of periodic Mathieu functions form an orthogonal set. We can show that the functions $ce_{2n}(t)$ and $se_{2n}(t)$ are orthogonal over the interval $(0, \pi)$. That is,

$$\left. \begin{array}{l} \int_0^\pi ce_{2n}(t)\, ce_{2m}(t)\, dt = 0 \\[2mm] \int_0^\pi se_{2n}(t)\, se_{2m}(t)\, dt = 0 \end{array} \right\} \quad n \neq m$$

$$\int_0^\pi ce_{2n}(t)\, se_{2m}(t)\, dt = 0.$$

To prove the last of these, for example, we write

$$\frac{d^2}{dt^2} ce_{2n}(t) + [\lambda_{2n}(h^2) - 2h^2 \cos 2t]\, ce_{2n}(t) = 0$$

$$\frac{d^2}{dt^2} se_{2m}(t) + [\lambda_{2m-1}(h^2) - 2h^2 \cos 2t]\, se_{2m}(t) = 0 \,.$$

We now multiply the first equation by $se_{2m}(t)$ and the second by $ce_{2n}(t)$ and subtract the second from the first:

$$se_{2m}(t) \frac{d^2}{dt^2} ce_{2n}(t) - ce_{2n}(t) \frac{d^2}{dt^2} se_{2m}(t) + [\lambda_{2n}(h^2) - \lambda_{2m-1}(h^2)]\, ce_{2n}(t)\, se_{2m}(t) = 0 \,.$$

If we integrate the equation over the interval $(0, \pi)$ and use integration by parts on the first two integrals we obtain

$$\left[se_{2m}(t) \frac{d}{dt} ce_{2n}(t) - ce_{2n}(t) \frac{d}{dt} se_{2m}(t) \right] \Big|_0^\pi$$

$$+ \left[\lambda_{2n}(h^2) - \lambda_{2m-1}(h^2) \right] \int_0^\pi ce_{2n}(t)\, se_{2m}(t)\, dt = 0 \,.$$

The integrated terms give a zero contribution since they are periodic and therefore take the same values at 0 and π. $\lambda_{2n}(h^2)$ and $\lambda_{2m-1}(h^2)$ are not equal and we see that

$$\int_0^\pi ce_{2n}(t)\, se_{2m}(t)\, dt = 0.$$

It is possible to expand functions in series of these orthogonal Mathieu functions. Suppose $f(t)$ is a function of period π. Then

$$f(t) = \sum_{n=0}^{\infty} a_n \, ce_{2n}(t) + \sum_{n=1}^{\infty} b_n \, se_{2n}(t),$$

where

$$a_n = \frac{\int_0^\pi f(t) \, ce_{2n}(t) \, dt}{\int_0^\pi [ce_{2n}(t)]^2 \, dt}$$

$$b_n = \frac{\int_0^\pi f(t) \, se_{2n}(t) \, dt}{\int_0^\pi [se_{2n}(t)]^2 \, dt}.$$

Exercises

1. Show that

$$ce_1(t) = \cos t - \frac{h^2}{8} \cos 3t + h^4 \left[\frac{1}{192} \cos 5t - \frac{1}{64} \cos 3t - \frac{1}{128} \cos t \right] + \cdots.$$

2. Investigate the equation

$$y'' + \lambda^2 \, Q(t) \, y = 0,$$

where
$$Q(t) = 1 \qquad 0 \le t < 1$$
$$= A^2 \qquad 1 \le t \le L$$

and $Q(t)$ is to be continued as an even periodic function of period $2L$ outside the interval $(0, L)$. Use the methods of Section 3.

Show that the characteristic equation has double roots so that two periodic solutions coexist for one value of λ if and only if $A(L - 1)$ is a rational number.

Bibliographical Appendix

Because of the great utility of the special functions the literature on them is vast. Unfortunately, much of it is hidden in books on physics and various topics in applied mathematics, and much can be found in research papers. Since this book is of a purely introductory character the reader will have to refer to more specialized treatises for more detailed information. The following list contains some of the more important and useful references, which in turn supply further references.

The following list is divided into five sublists. The first one consists of books of a general character that treat some or all of the topics covered in this book. The remaining four sublists consist of references that pertain to the four topics covered in this book.

General References

Erdélyi, A., Magnus, W., Oberhettinger, F., and Tricomi, F. G., *Higher Transcendental Functions*, Vols. I, II, III. McGraw-Hill, 1953.

Jahnke, F. and Emde, F., *Tables of Functions with Formulae and Curves*, 4th Ed. New York, 1945.

Lense, Josef, *Reihenentwicklungen in der mathematischen Physik*, 3d Ed. de Gruyter, 1953.

Magnus, W. and Oberhettinger, F., *Formulas and Theorems for the Special Functions of Mathematical Physics*. New York, 1949.

Rainville, Earl D., *Special Functions*. Macmillan, 1960.

Sneddon, Ian N. *Special Functions of Mathematical Physics and Chemistry*. Oliver and Boyd, 1956.

Truesdell, C. A. *Special Functions*, Annals of Mathematical Studies No. 18. Princeton, 1948.

Whittaker, E. T. and Watson, G. N., *A Course of Modern Analysis*, 4th Ed. Cambridge, 1947.

Orthogonal Polynomials

Jackson, Dunham, *Fourier Series and Orthogonal Polynomials*, Carus Mathematical Monograph No. 6, 1957.

Kaczmarz, S. and Steinhaus, H., *Theorie der Orthogonalreihen*. New York, 1951.

Szegö, G., *Orthogonal Polynomials*, American Mathematical Society Colloquium Publications, Vol. 23. New York, 1939.

Legendre Functions

Hobson, E. W., *The Theory of Spherical and Ellipsoidal Harmonics*. Cambridge, 1931.

MacRobert, T. M., *Spherical Harmonics*. London, 1928.

Bessel Functions

Gray, A., Mathews, G. B., and MacRobert, T. M., *Bessel Functions*. London, 1922.

McLachlan, N. W., *Bessel Functions for Engineers*. Oxford, 1946.

Watson, G. N., *A Treatise on the Theory of Bessel Functions*, 2d Ed. Cambridge, 1948.

Weyrich, Rudolf, *Die Zylinderfunktionen und ihre Anwendungen*. Teubner, 1937.

Mathieu Functions

McLachlan, N. W., *Theory and Application of Mathieu Functions*. Oxford, 1947.

Meixner, J. and Schäfke, F. W., *Mathieusche Funktionen und Sphäroidfunktionen*. Springer, 1954.

Strutt, M. J. O., *Lamésche, Mathieusche und Verwandte Funktionen in Physik und Technik*. Ergebnisse der Mathematik und ihrer Grenzgebiete, Vol. I, No. 3. Berlin, 1933.

Index

Index